HEMISPHERICAL PROJECTION METHODS IN ROCK MECHANICS

S. D. Priest

*Imperial College of Science and Technology,
London SW7*

London
GEORGE ALLEN & UNWIN
Boston   Sydney

Preface

The aim of this book is to explain in simple terms a number of graphical methods, based upon the concept of hemispherical projection, that allow the plotting and analysis of three-dimensional quantities in two dimensions on a sheet of paper. These methods, which are commonly referred to as stereographic projection methods, provide an important tool for the plotting and analysis of the structural features that control the behaviour of jointed or fractured rock masses. Despite the availability of computers, these methods are becoming widely used in rock mechanics studies since they offer an immediate visual appreciation of a given structural problem and provide a rapid solution with a precision that is more than adequate for most applications.

Much of this book is based upon a series of ten lectures given to students attending the MSc course in Engineering Rock Mechanics at the Imperial College of Science and Technology, London. The book has been designed to take the reader in easy stages from an elementary level to a comprehensive understanding of relatively advanced methods of hemispherical projection applied to rock mechanics problems. To this end, great reliance is placed on the use of worked examples and graded exercises. The examples are supplemented by diagrams, drawn at full scale, so that the reader can check his answer simply by overlaying his construction on the appropriate diagram. Concise summaries of the more advanced techniques are provided for easy reference when working through these examples and exercises.

Most of the methods explained in this book, particularly in the later chapters, are totally original and cannot be found in any other publications. The author is indebted to MSc students who attended the MSc course in engineering rock mechanics between 1977 and 1984 for their criticisms and comments concerning these new methods and for suggesting more effective ways of explaining them. The author is also grateful to Professor P. B. Attewell, Dr J. W. Bray, Dr J. A. Hudson and Dr J. O. Watson for helpful comments during the early stages of preparing this book, to Mr A. J. Dutton for checking the examples and exercises, to Dr J. W. Cosgrove and Dr G. A. Watt for their critical reviews of the text, and also to Miss M. Knox for typing the manuscript. Finally, the author expresses his gratitude to Mr R. Jones and Mr G. D. Palmer of George Allen & Unwin for their help during the editorial and production stages, and to Professor E. T. Brown not only for his valuable comments but also for his encouragement and support throughout the preparation of this book.

S.D.P.

© S. D. Priest, 1985
This book is copyright under the Berne Convention. No reproduction without permission. All rights reserved.

George Allen & Unwin (Publishers) Ltd,
40 Museum Street, London WC1A 1LU, UK

George Allen & Unwin (Publishers) Ltd,
Park Lane, Hemel Hempstead, Herts HP2 4TE, UK

Allen & Unwin Inc.,
9 Winchester Terrace, Winchester, Mass 01890, USA

George Allen & Unwin Australia Pty Ltd,
8 Napier Street, North Sydney, NSW 2060, Australia

First published in 1985

British Library Cataloguing in Publication Data

Priest, S. D.
 Hemispherical projection methods in rock mechanics
1. Rock mechanics—Graphic methods
2. Projection
I. Title
624.1'5132   TA706
ISBN 0-04-622007-0

Library of Congress Cataloging in Publication Data

Priest, S. D. (Stephen Donald), 1950–
 Hemispherical projection methods in rock mechanics.
Bibliography: p.
Includes index.
1. Rock mechanics—Graphic methods. 2. Spherical projection. I. Title.
TA706.P74 1985   624.1'5132   84-11182
ISBN 0-04-622007-0 (pbk.)

Set in 10 on 12 point Times by Mathematical Composition Setters Ltd, Salisbury and printed in Great Britain by Butler and Tanner Ltd, Frome and London

Contents

List of tables

For Rosie and Robert

1 Introduction and definitions

1.1 Introduction

Hemispherical projection is a graphical method whereby data on the three-dimensional orientation of planar and linear features can be presented and analysed in two dimensions on a sheet of paper. The method is often referred to as 'stereographic projection', which literally means the projection of solid or three-dimensional drawings. Hemispherical projection methods are widely used in rock mechanics studies for analysing planar discontinuities, such as fractures, faults, fissures and bedding planes that occur at various orientations within rock masses. Such analysis may include not only data collection and presentation but also the determination of the stability of rock blocks exposed at rock faces.

A number of authors have published accounts of hemispherical projection methods used in geological or rock mechanics studies, notably Phillips (1971), Ragan (1973), Goodman (1976, 1980), Hoek and Brown (1980) and Hoek and Bray (1981). The texts by Goodman (1976) and by Hoek and Brown (1980) also contain some information on the practical aspects of measuring discontinuities in the field. This will be of value to those readers who do not have any practical geological training.

Hemispherical projection methods are of great value in rock mechanics studies because they present structural data as a graphical representation rather than as a numerical abstraction. The human brain is highly skilled at taking in graphical information and is able to remember fairly complex graphical construction methods. It is unfortunate, however, that an unambiguous written explanation of even a relatively simple graphical method can sound impossibly complex. Once a method has been mastered, however, it is usually very easy to remember it in graphical terms, so that the complex written explanation can be forgotten. To help in this process a number of worked examples are included to explain the methods. These examples are supplemented by exercises at the end of each chapter.

One major criticism of hemispherical projection, and indeed all graphical, methods is that they can be imprecise. It is the author's experience that, by exercising reasonable care, results within $\pm 2^\circ$ of the correct orientation can be obtained consistently. Such precision is usually adequate for rock mechanics studies since natural discontinuities and other features are rarely truly planar throughout a rock mass. This means that orientation measurements taken in the field are usually themselves distributed quite widely about a mean value.

1.2 Definitions

Before proceeding with the methods of hemispherical projection it is necessary to define the terms used. In order to assist the reader in visualising the geometrical relationships, angles will usually be expressed in degrees throughout this book. The orientation of any given line in three-dimensional space can be recorded unambiguously in terms of its trend α and plunge β, defined as follows:

(a) Plunge, β $(-90^\circ \leqslant \beta \leqslant 90^\circ)$ The acute angle, measured in a vertical plane, between a given line and the horizontal. By convention, a line directed with a downward sense has a positive plunge; a line with an upward sense has a negative plunge.

(b) Trend, α $(0^\circ \leqslant \alpha \leqslant 360^\circ)$ The geographical azimuth, measured in clockwise rotation from north (0°), of the vertical plane containing the given line of plunge β. By convention, trend is measured in the direction of plunge.

These terms are illustrated in Figure 1.1. The downward-directed end of the line in this figure has a trend 065° and plunge 37°; the upward-directed end of the line has a trend 245° (i.e. $065^\circ + 180^\circ$) and a plunge -37°. In most cases it is unnecessary to record whether a line has a downward or an upward sense, since it is only the *orientation* of the feature that is important. In view of this, only the positive (i.e. downward) value of plunge, and the associated trend,

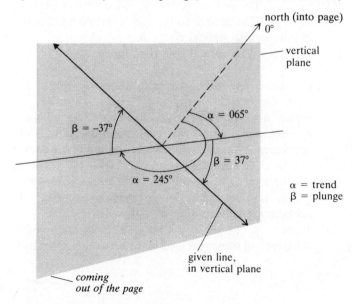

Figure 1.1 Definition of trend and plunge.

1

will be used throughout this book. The orientation of a given line is usually recorded in terms of α and β as a three-digit and a two-digit number separated by a slash (e.g. 247/68).

The following notation is used for the trend and plunge of linear features that may be encountered in rock mechanics studies:

(a) α, β General or unspecified line.

(b) α_d, β_d The line of maximum dip of an inclined plane. This is the imaginary line in a given non-horizontal plane whose plunge exceeds that of all other lines in the plane. To understand this and subsequent definitions fully, it is necessary to visualise a plane as being composed of an infinite number of coplanar lines radiating from a point. One of these lines will be the line of maximum dip. The orientation of an inclined planar feature is usually recorded in terms of α_d and β_d as a three-digit and a two-digit number in the format explained above. In such cases α_d is called the 'dip direction' and β_d the 'angle of dip' or 'dip amount' of the plane. The dip direction and the angle of dip of a given inclined plane can be measured in the field by means of some suitable compass–clinometer device, as explained by Hoek and Brown (1980).

(c) α_{di}, β_{di} The line of maximum dip of the ith discontinuity plane.

(d) α_{df}, β_{df} The line of maximum dip of a rock face.

(e) α_n, β_n The normal to a plane. This is the imaginary line constructed at right angles to a given plane. The normal is sometimes called the 'pole to a plane'. This rather confusing use of the word 'pole' will not be adopted in this book. For a given plane, $\alpha_n = \alpha_d \pm 180°$, $0° \leqslant \alpha_n \leqslant 360°$. Also $\beta_n = 90° - \beta_d$.

(f) α_{ni}, β_{ni} The normal to the ith discontinuity plane.

(g) α_{nh}, β_{nh} The normal to the horizontal plane; this is, of course, the vertical direction.

(h) α_{nf}, β_{nf} The normal to a rock face.

Some further definitions are as follows:

(i)   Strike, α_t The geographical azimuth of an imaginary horizontal line in a given inclined plane. For convenience, the azimuth of only one end of the strike line need be recorded, hence $0° \leqslant \alpha_t \leqslant 180°$. For a given plane, $\alpha_t = \alpha_d - 90°$ ($\pm 180°$) and $\alpha_t = \alpha_n - 90°$ ($\pm 180°$), The angles in parentheses are used, if necessary, to ensure that $0° \leqslant \alpha_t \leqslant 180°$.

(j)   Pitch, γ ($-90° \leqslant \gamma \leqslant 90°$)   The acute angle measured in some specified plane between a given line

and the strike of the plane. As with plunge, lines directed downwards from the horizontal have a positive pitch; lines directed upwards have a negative pitch. It is important to record the direction of pitch, i.e. from which end of the strike line the angle of pitch has been measured. For this purpose it is sufficient to specify the geographical quadrant (north-east, south-east, etc.) rather than the exact azimuth of the strike line.

Figure 1.2 shows a plane of dip direction/dip amount 215/63 (α_d/β_d). the normal to this plane has a trend/plunge 035/27 (α_n/β_n) and the strike of the plane is 125° (α_t). A line with a pitch of 41° from the north-west end of the strike of the plane has a trend/plunge 284/36. The calculation of this latter orientation was done using hemispherical projection methods.

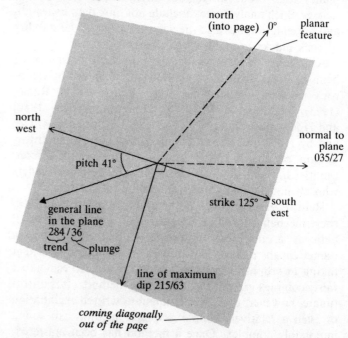

Figure 1.2   Orientation of a plane.

Exercises

1.1   A plane has a dip direction/dip amount 325/72. What is the trend/plunge of its normal?

1.2   A plane has a strike of 133° and an angle of dip 27°. What are the possible orientations of its normal?

1.3   The normal to a plane has a trend/plunge 116/64. What is the strike of the plane?

Answers to these exercises are given on page 123.

2 Polar and equatorial projection

2.1 Polar projection

The principle of all projection methods is that the orientation of a line in three-dimensional space is uniquely represented by the position of a point within a two-dimensional area called the 'area of projection'. The process of converting from three to two dimensions is called 'projection' because it is similar to the process of casting a two-dimensional shadow of a three-dimensional object using a light projector. In hemispherical projection, the area of projection is a circle of some convenient radius (R) constructed on a sheet of paper. The 12 o'clock position on the perimeter of this circle represents the north direction (azimuth $0°$), the 3 o'clock position is east (azimuth $90°$), the 6 o'clock position is south (azimuth $180°$) and the 9 o'clock position is west (azimuth $270°$). A line that has a plunge of $90°$ projects as a point at the centre of the circle; a line with a plunge close to $0°$ projects as a point near the perimeter, at an azimuth corresponding to its trend. The radial distance (r) of the point, measured from the centre of the circle, is therefore some function of the plunge (β) of the line that it represents. The exact form of the functional relation between r and β depends upon the method of projection used.

The basis of all commonly used projection methods is an imaginary sphere (the 'reference sphere'), of radius R,

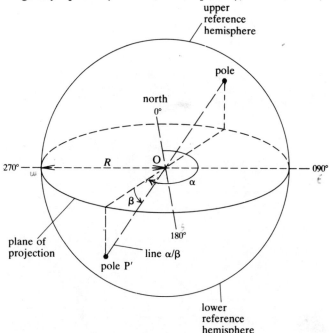

Figure 2.1 The reference sphere, intersected by a line of trend α and plunge β.

positioned with its centre at the centre of the area of projection. An imaginary line, parallel to the given line of trend α and plunge β, is positioned so that it passes through the centre of the sphere, with its trend direction at the correct azimuth (Fig. 2.1.). The line, if extended, intersects the reference sphere at two points or 'poles'. The position of any point on the reference sphere bears a unique relation to the orientation of the line that produced it. This position can be transferred or projected onto any convenient plane. In this case the plane of projection is a horizontal plane that passes through the centre of the reference sphere. In later chapters, however, the plane of projection is chosen so that it is parallel to some other relevant plane, such as the face of an excavation. A horizontal plane of projection cuts the reference sphere into an upper and lower hemisphere. The upper hemisphere, which is associated only with lines of negative plunge, will not be required since all orientations are taken to have positive values of plunge throughout this book. The point, or pole, on the lower hemisphere can be projected onto the horizontal plane of projection by a number of different methods. Two of these methods are illustrated in Figure 2.2 by means of vertical sections, in a plane of strike direction α, taken through the lower reference hemisphere and passing through its centre.

Figure 2.2a illustrates an equal-angle projection. The given line of trend α and downward (positive) plunge β intersects the lower reference hemisphere at point P$'$. The projection is achieved by drawing a straight line from P$'$ to a point T, which is a distance R vertically above the centre O of the reference hemisphere. The projection of P$'$ occurs at P where this straight line passes through the plane of projection. For this projection the relation between r, the radial distance of point P from O, and β is given by

$$r = R \tan \left(\frac{90 - \beta}{2} \right) \qquad (2.1)$$

or

$$r = \frac{R(1 + k) \cos \beta}{1 + k + \sin \beta} \qquad (2.2)$$

where, in this case, $k = 0$.

Figure 2.2b illustrates an equal-area projection. As before, the given line intersects the lower reference hemisphere at point P$'$. This point is projected by swinging it in a vertical plane through a circular arc centred on point B, which is a distance R vertically below the centre of the reference hemisphere. The projection of P$'$ occurs

3

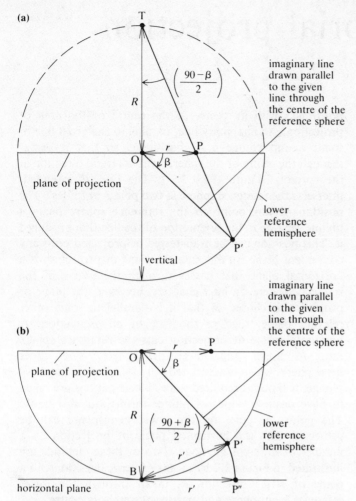

(a)

(b)

Figure 2.2 Vertical sections through the centre of the lower reference hemisphere, illustrating (a) equal-angle projection and (b) equal-area projection.

at P″ where this circular arc intersects the horizontal plane constructed through the point B. The radial distance r' of the point P″ from B is given by

$$r' = 2R \cos\left(\frac{90 + \beta}{2}\right) \quad (2.3)$$

When $\beta = 0°$, $r' = 2R \cos 45° = R\sqrt{2}$. This means that the radius of the resultant projection is larger, by a factor $\sqrt{2}$, than the radius of the reference hemisphere. The point P″ is, therefore, transferred to point P, a distance r from the centre of the plane of projection, by letting $r = r'/\sqrt{2}$. Hence

$$r = R\sqrt{2} \cos\left(\frac{90 + \beta}{2}\right) \quad (2.4)$$

The process of equal-area projection is rather like 'peeling the skin' off the lower reference hemisphere, flattening it out and then shrinking it to a circle of radius R.

An approximation of the equal-area projection can be

generated using a similar method to that described for the equal-angle projection. For an equal-area projection, however, the point T is located a distance $R(1 + \sqrt{2})$ vertically above O. In this case the relation between r and β is given, approximately, by Equation 2.2 setting $k = \sqrt{2}$.

The different properties of equal-angle and equal-area projections are best understood by considering a circle, of radius R_s', centred on a radial line through point P′ on the surface of the lower reference hemisphere. If R_s' is less than R, the circle is called a 'small circle'. Such a circle is generated by a conical shape, radiating from the centre of the reference hemisphere, with a semi-apex angle

$$\delta = \arcsin(R_s'/R)$$

measured from the axis OP′ as shown in Figure 2.3. It is demonstrated in Appendix A.1 that the equal-angle projection of this small circle is itself a circle. However, unless $\beta = 90°$, the projected circle is not centred on the equal-angle projection of P′. The radius R_s of the projection of the small circle is given by

$$R_s = R\left[\tan\left(\frac{90 - \beta + \delta}{2}\right) - \tan\left(\frac{90 - \beta - \delta}{2}\right)\right]\Big/2 \quad (2.5)$$

where $\delta < 90° + \beta$.

Equation 2.5 shows that, for a given value of δ, the radius R_s, and hence the area of the small circle, decreases with increasing plunge β of the line OP′. In practical terms

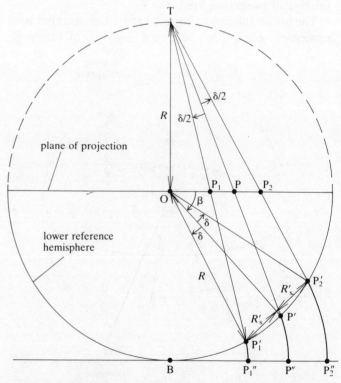

Figure 2.3 Vertical section through the centre of the reference sphere, illustrating the projection of a small circle.

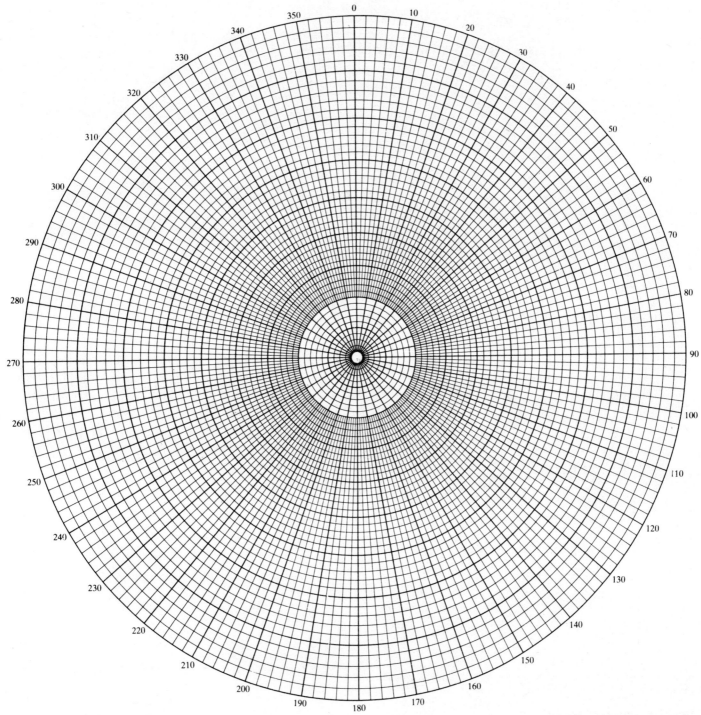

Figure 2.4 Polar equal-angle net.

this means that a pair of lines inclined at some small solid angle 2δ to each other will plot closer together if they plunge steeply than if they plunge at some shallow angle. The significance of this distortion in the equal-angle projection when interpreting discontinuity data is discussed later in this chapter.

Before leaving the equal-angle projection it is worth while considering one explanation of why the term 'equal angle' is appropriate. The lines OP_1' and OP_2', in the same

vertical plane as OP' in Figure 2.3, make an angle 2δ at the centre of the lower reference hemisphere. The points P_1' and P_2' project to define the points P_1 and P_2 which subtend a constant angle δ at point T for *all* values of β. Hence, for a given value of δ, the points P_1 and P_2 will always subtend an *equal angle* at T, whatever the value of β.

It can be shown that the equal-area projection of the small circle takes the shape of a fourth-order curve, except

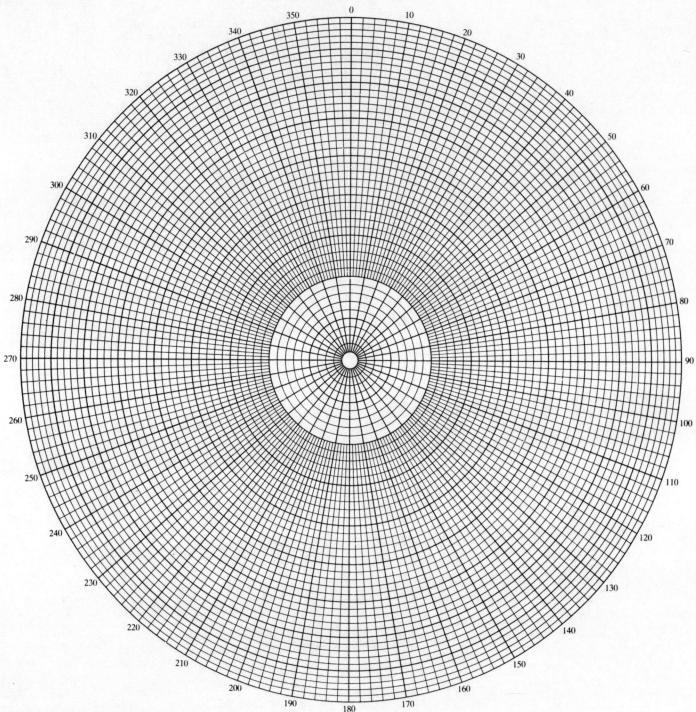

Figure 2.5 Polar equal-area net.

when $\beta = 90°$, in which case the projection is itself circular with a radius

$$R_s = R\sqrt{2}\cos\left(\frac{180 - \delta}{2}\right).$$

The important feature of the equal-area projection is that, for a given value of δ, the area enclosed by the projection of the associated small circle is constant for all values of

β. The equal-area projection does not, therefore, suffer from the areal distortion of the equal-angle projection. This property of the equal-area projection is discussed further in Appendix A.2.

It is impracticable to have to use Equations 2.1 to 2.4 to calculate the radial co-ordinates of each point to be plotted. For this reason, circular grids have been developed to facilitate the plotting procedure. These grids are called 'polar projections' or 'polar nets' because the lines on them look rather like the lines of longitude and latitude on a globe of the world when viewed along the polar axis. Since the similarity is only visual the reader is not advised, at this stage, to explore the geometrical implications of the analogy. The lines of 'longitude' on the polar net are radial lines giving the azimuth direction of trend, usually at intervals of 2°. The lines of 'latitude' are concentric circles with radii computed using either Equation 2.1, 2.2 or 2.4 giving plunge, again at intervals of 2°. Figure 2.4 shows a polar equal-angle net (Eqn 2.1) and Figure 2.5 shows a polar equal-area net (Eqn 2.4.).

Apart from the distortion referred to earlier, it is of little consequence which type of net is used to plot the orientation of a line in space. It *is* important, however, to maintain consistency in the use of one type of projection. To avoid marking the net, it is desirable to overlay it with a sheet of tracing paper. The resulting diagram will then be free from the radial and concentric construction lines of the net. It is, of course, possible to plot a point representing the orientation of a given line, of trend α and plunge β, without using a polar net. This can be achieved by first constructing a plotting circle of radius R with the azimuth values of trend α marked round the perimeter at suitable intervals. A cursor of length R is then constructed and graduated in values of plunge β using either of the Equations 2.1, 2.2. or 2.4. This cursor is then fixed radially, using a drawing pin at the centre of the plotting circle, so that the cursor is free to rotate. This arrangement, shown diagrammatically in Figure 2.6, allows points to be plotted rapidly and accurately without using a polar net.

In rock mechanics studies, polar nets are used for plotting the normals to discontinuities sampled during a rock mass survey. During such a survey the orientations of perhaps 200 or 300 discontinuity planes will have been recorded as the trend and downward plunge of their line of maximum dip (α_d/β_d). To save time, the calculation of the trend and plunge of the normal can be done during the plotting process itself, while at the same time dispensing with the need for a polar net. This is done using the plotting circle and radial cursor described above. The conversion from trend and plunge of the line of maximum dip to trend and plunge of the normal to the plane is simply achieved by temporarily relabelling the graduations on the plotting circle and the cursor as follows. The plotting circle azimuth values are changed by 180° so that 0° becomes 180°, 090° becomes 270°, 180° becomes 0° and 270° becomes 090°, etc. In other words, the plotting circle is simply rotated through 180°. The angles on the cursor are subtracted from 90°, so that 90° becomes 0°, 80° becomes 10°, ..., and 0° becomes 90°. The α_d/β_d values can now be plotted directly using the temporary scales. When the temporary plotting circle scale is removed and replaced by the original one, each point will represent the orientation of the normal to the plane. Several hundred normals can be plotted in less than an hour using this method. The resulting diagram is of great value since it gives a visual impression of the discontinuity fabric of the rock mass.

In many cases, discontinuities tend to be orientated in subparallel groups or 'sets'; this leads to a clustering of their normals on the projection. Since the projection method itself can produce an apparent clustering of normals that have a large plunge it is desirable to plot normals using the equal-area projection (Eqn 2.4) which removes this areal distortion. The identification of discontinuity sets is of considerable importance in rock mechanics studies. Various methods have been developed, therefore, for analysing and emphasising visually the clusters of normals. These methods are discussed in Chapter 5.

The polar projection is ideally suited for plotting points, but is of little value in analysing the three-dimensional geometry produced by inclined planes. In order to analyse planes it is necessary to be able to plot the locus of points that represent the infinite number of lines in those planes. Since this cannot be done easily on a polar projection, it is necessary to use a different type of projection: the equatorial projection.

2.2 Equatorial projection

An equatorial projection is designed to permit the plotting and analysis of planes, as well as lines, of various orientations. The principles of hemispherical projection used in constructing equatorial projections are exactly the same as those described in the previous section for polar projec-

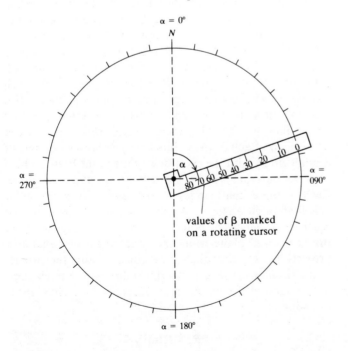

Figure 2.6 The use of a rotating cursor to plot directly points representing lines of trend/plunge α/β.

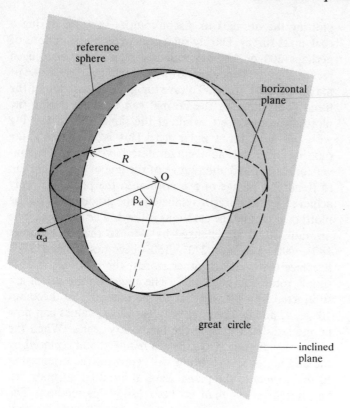

Figure 2.7 The great circle of an inclined plane.

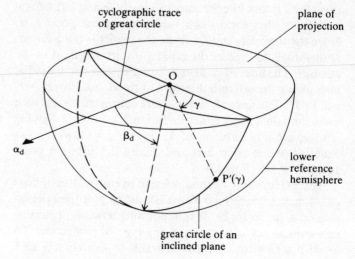

Figure 2.8 The cyclographic trace of a great circle.

tions. In particular, the projection can be generated using either the equal-angle or the equal-area constructions.

Figure 2.7 shows an inclined plane, of dip direction/dip amount α_d/β_d, positioned so that it passes through the centre O of the reference sphere of radius R. The circle, produced by the intersection of the inclined plane with the reference sphere also has a radius R and is called a 'great circle'. It has already been noted that circles with a radius of less than R on the reference sphere are called 'small circles'.

Figure 2.8 shows half of the great circle, generated where the inclined plane intersects the lower reference hemisphere. This inclined plane can be visualised as being composed of an infinite number of lines OP'(γ), of downward pitch γ, radiating from the centre point O. Two special lines OP'(0°) and OP'(90°) are respectively the strike and the line of maximum dip of the inclined plane. The great circle is therefore the locus of points P'(γ). Each of these points can be projected onto the horizontal plane, using the equal-angle or equal-area constructions described in Section 2.1, to give the locus of points P(γ). This locus is called the 'cyclographic trace' or, more simply, the 'great circle' of the inclined plane. On an equal-angle projection, the cyclographic trace of the great circle of an inclined plane of dip direction/dip amount α_d/β_d is, in fact, part of a circular arc of radius

$$R_g = R/\cos\beta_d$$

which has its centre at a radial distance

$$r_g = R\tan\beta_d$$

from the centre of the projection measured along a radial line of azimuth $\alpha_d \pm 180°$. This construction is shown in Figure 2.9a. On an equal-area construction, the great circle projects as part of a fourth-order curve. Whatever projection method is used, the great circle of any vertical plane projects as a diametral line on the projection ($R_g = \infty$), while a horizontal plane projects onto the perimeter of the circle of projection.

Consider again the inclined plane of dip direction/dip amount α_d/β_d, but this time construct only a finite number of lines OP'(γ); for example OP'(0°), OP'(10°), OP'(20°),..., OP'(80°), OP'(90°) where γ is measured downwards from both ends of the strike line. This will generate a number of points P'(γ) on the great circle, each associated with a particular value of pitch γ (Fig. 2.10). Imagine, now, that the inclined plane is rotated about its strike line so that it sweeps round the entire lower hemisphere. Each of the points P'(γ) will trace out half of a small circle, with the exception of the point P'(0°) which does not move, and P'(90°) which traces out a great circle. Each of these small circles is associated with a particular value of pitch angle γ. Again, each small circle can be regarded as a locus of points, which can be projected onto the horizontal plane using the equal-angle or equal-area projections. On an equal-angle construction, the projection of a small circle, generated by a line with a pitch angle γ in a plane with a dip direction α_d, is part of a circular arc of radius

$$R_s = R\tan\gamma$$

which has its centre at a radial distance

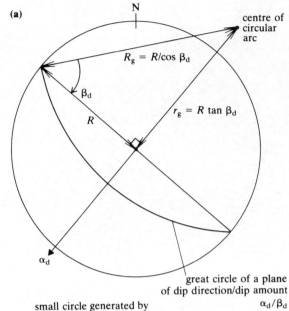

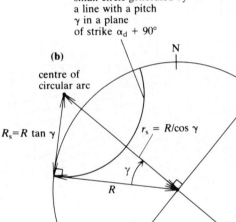

Figure 2.9 Equal-angle construction of (a) great circles and (b) small circles.

$$r_s = R/\cos \gamma$$

from the centre of the projection measured along a line of azimuth $\alpha_d \pm 90°$. This construction is shown in Figure 2.9b. On an equal-area projection, the small circle projects as part of a fourth-order curve. The important, and useful, property of a small circle is that it describes the changing orientation of a given line when it is rotated about a given axis. The small circles described above are special in that their axes of rotation are horizontal. The ability to rotate a line about a given axis is of considerable importance in rock mechanics studies.

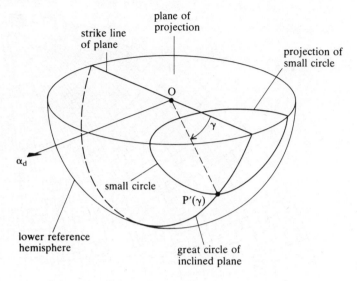

Figure 2.10 The definition of a small circle.

In many cases it is impracticable to use the constructions explained above and in Figure 2.9 to generate the equal-angle projections of great circles and small circles. Moreover, their construction on an equal-area projection would involve lengthy computations in three-dimensional geometry. To overcome this problem, circular grids have been developed to facilitate the plotting procedure. These grids are called 'equatorial projections', 'equatorial nets' or, sometimes, 'meridional projections'. This is because the projections of great circles look like the lines of longitude (or meridians) and the projections of small circles look rather like the lines of latitude on a globe of the world viewed from above the equator. It is impracticable to construct an equatorial projection that contains the great circles for planes of all orientations. Instead, the great circles of planes with a north–south strike only are constructed, usually at $2°$ intervals of dip angle. Similarly, only those small circles generated by lines of various pitch angles in these north–south striking planes are constructed, again usually at $2°$ intervals of pitch angle. Figure 2.11 shows an equatorial equal-angle net, and Figure 2.12 shows an equatorial equal-area net. Each of these nets contains only two straight lines: the north–south and east–west diameters. The former represents the great circle of a vertical plane with a north–south strike. The latter is generated by a line with a pitch of $90°$ in a plane with a north–south strike as it is rotated about this strike axis. This east–west diameter is special since it is also the great circle of a vertical plane with an east–west strike. In order to use the nets effectively, it is advisable to plot the great circles onto an overlay of tracing paper. This makes it possible to plot a plane of any general orientation by rotating the tracing paper until the plane has its strike temporarily on the north–south diameter of the net. The use of an equatorial net in this way allows it to fulfil all of the functions of a polar net. Again, it is of little consequence

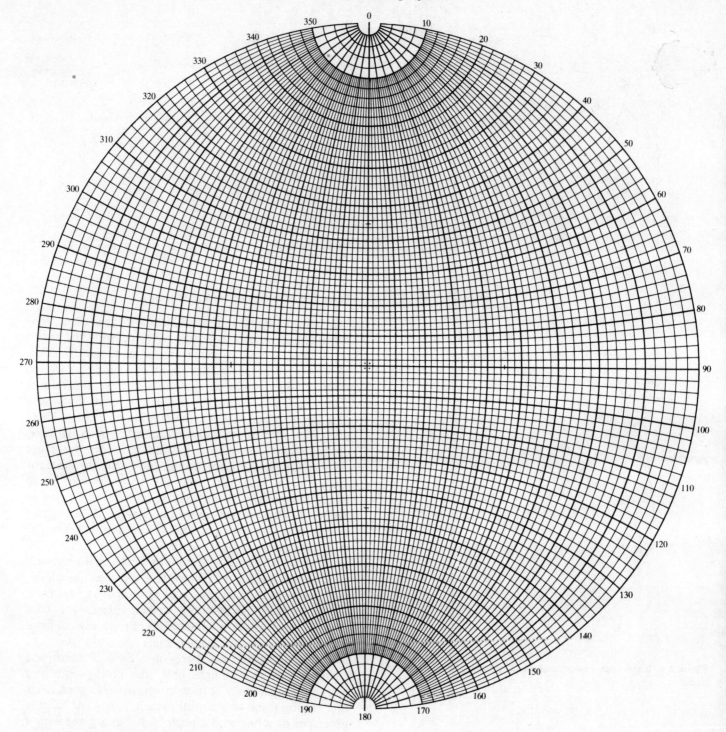

Figure 2.11 Equatorial equal-angle net.

whether an equal-angle or an equal-area equatorial net is used as long as one type or the other is used consistently. Many workers advocate the use of the equal-angle net, arguing that its circular arcs facilitate a more precise construction of great circles and small circles; others recommend the equal-area net since its lack of areal distortion makes it ideal for interpreting and analysing plots of discontinuity normals. Unless a large proportion of the work involves the plotting and analysis of discontinuity (or other) normals, it is probably desirable to use an equal-angle net since, by using the construction in Figure 2.9, there is no reliance on the availability of printed nets of a suitable radius. This could be of crucial importance when working in the field. All future work in this book will be carried out on a lower-hemisphere equal-angle equatorial net.

10

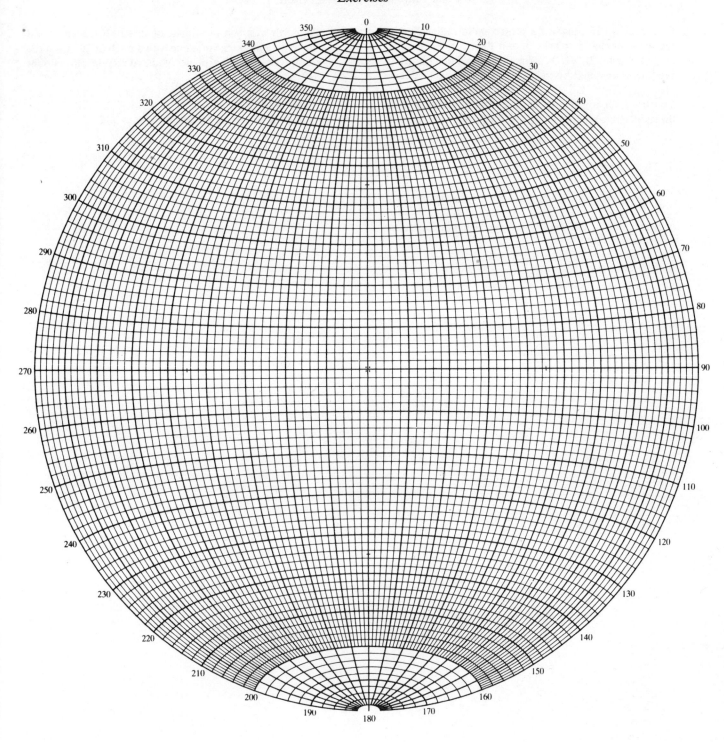

Figure 2.12 Equatorial equal-area net.

Exercises

2.1 A point plots 50 mm from the centre of a lower-hemisphere projection of radius 100 mm. What is the plunge of the line represented by this point if this were (i) an equal-angle projection and (ii) an equal-area projection?

2.2 A cone with a semi-apex angle of $5°$ has its apex at the centre of a reference hemisphere of radius 90 mm. The cone, which has an axis of plunge β, intersects the reference hemisphere to define a small circle. Calculate the area of the equal-angle projection of this small circle when (i) $\beta = 5°$ and (ii) $\beta = 90°$.

11

2.3 [1] Construct, on an equal-angle projection of radius 90 mm, the great circles of planes of dip direction/dip amount (1) 113/35 and (2) 197/28. What is the trend and plunge of the line represented by the point of intersection of these great circles?

2.4 [1] Construct, on an equal-angle projection of radius 90 mm, the small circle generated by a line with a pitch of 29° from the north-west end of a plane of strike 130°. Hence, find the trend and plunge of a line with a pitch of 29° from the north-west end of a plane of dip direction/dip amount 040/37.

Answers to these exercises are given on page 123.

---

[1] These exercises should be carried out using the compass construction methods illustrated in Figure 2.9.

3 Basic procedures using hemispherical projection

3.1 Introduction

The equal-angle or equal-area equatorial nets, described in the previous chapter, can be used for plotting lines and planes of any orientation. The reader is advised to photocopy the equal-angle net in Figure 2.11, and then stick the copy to a suitable reinforcing backing, so that he can work through the examples and exercises in this and subsequent chapters. It is now necessary to overlay the net with a sheet of tracing paper capable of rotating about the centre. This can be achieved by pressing a drawing pin up through the centre of the net and then impaling the tracing paper so that it is free to rotate, as shown in Figure 3.1. Before commencing any plotting it is important to mark the north point on the tracing paper (azimuth 0°); this is usually labelled 'N'. Some workers also recommend that the perimeter of the net should be copied onto the tracing paper. Although this gives a neater result it is not strictly necessary. If required, however, this circle is best plotted separately using a pair of compasses. Since a lower-hemisphere projection will be used throughout, it will only be possible to plot lines with a downward (i.e. positive) plunge within this plotting circle. Throughout this and subsequent chapters, the construction on the tracing paper overlay will be referred to as the 'projection'; the grid beneath will be referred to as the 'net'.

3.2 Plotting a line of trend/plunge α/β

The definitions of trend and plunge given in Chapter 1 are the key to plotting a point representing a line of some given orientation. The trend α is the azimuth of the vertical plane containing the given line of plunge β. On the equatorial net there are two great circles representing vertical planes: the north–south and the east–west diameters of the net. Although either of these diameters can be used in the plotting process, it is generally desirable to use the east–west diameter only. In order to utilise this diameter, it is first necessary to rotate the tracing paper overlay until the trend direction of the line being plotted lies temporarily on the east–west diameter. Angles of plunge can then be counted from the perimeter of the net, along this diameter, using the great circles (the 'lines of longitude') on the net as graduations. Points on the east–west diameter of the net represent the lines of maximum dip of the group of planes, with a north–south strike, that generate the great circles on the net. The angles of plunge counted along the east–west diameter are, therefore, the same as the angles of dip of these special planes. The plotting procedure is explained below using simple examples.

Example 3.1 (Fig. 3.2[1]) Plot, on a lower-hemisphere projection, the point representing a line of trend/plunge 219/68.

The line in this example has a trend 219° and plunge 68°. The first step is to set up the tracing paper over the net and to mark carefully the north point 'N'. With this north point at its home position, the azimuth 219° is marked on the perimeter of the projection by a small radial line. If several points are to be plotted, it can be helpful to label this mark with the actual azimuth value, as shown in

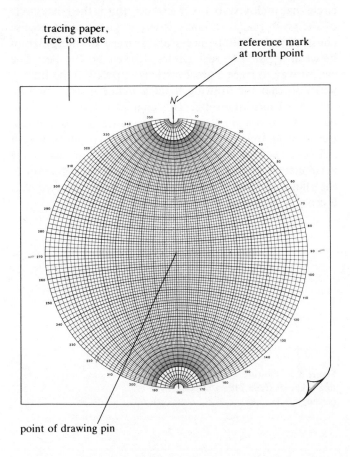

Figure 3.1 The use of a tracing-paper overlay with the net.

tracing paper, free to rotate

reference mark at north point

point of drawing pin

---

[1] The projections associated with this and subsequent examples are drawn to the same scale as the net in Figure 2.11. The reader can, therefore, check his answer simply by overlaying his construction on the appropriate diagram.

Figure 3.2a. The tracing paper is next rotated until this azimuth mark lies at either end of the east–west diameter of the net. The plunge angle 68° is then counted from the azimuth mark on the perimeter along this diameter to give the required point, L, as shown in Figure 3.2b. Finally, the north point is returned to its home position.

(a) α = 219°

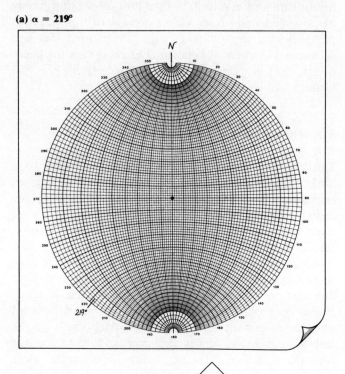

(b) β = 68°

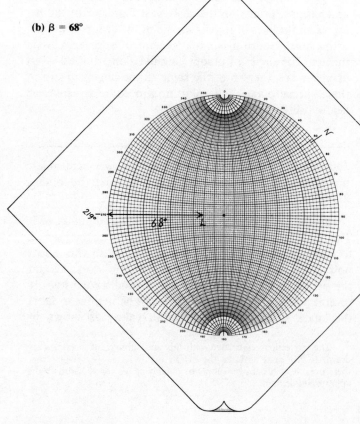

In some cases it may be necessary to find the trend and plunge of the line represented by some point that is already plotted on the projection. The procedure is the reverse of that described above. The tracing paper is first rotated until the given point lies on the east–west diameter of the net. The azimuth mark is then drawn at the intersection between this diameter and the perimeter of the net, ensuring that the azimuth mark lies on the same radius as the given point. The acute angle between the given point and the perimeter is then counted along the east–west diameter, to give the angle of plunge of the line that it represents. When the north point is returned to its home position, the azimuth mark gives the trend of the line.

3.3 Plotting a plane of dip direction/dip amount α_d/β_d

The process of plotting the great circle and the normal to a plane is an extension of the plotting procedure for a line. The first step is to plot the point, D, representing the line of maximum dip of the plane, as shown in Figure 3.3a. This is done using the method described above, but this time the line has a trend α_d and plunge β_d. With the resulting point still on the east–west diameter, the great circle that is closest to it is traced off; this is the great circle of the given plane. In many cases, to give a more precise construction, it will be necessary to trace an interpolation between a pair of great circles marked on the net. The easiest way to trace a great circle is to position the tracing paper so that the drawing hand is diametrically opposite the line of maximum dip. This enables the great circle to be drawn with a single sweep of the hand, pivoting about the wrist and elbow. It is usually helpful to mark with a tick the points where the great circle intersects the perimeter of the net since this gives the strike direction of the plane. The line of maximum dip is usually marked with a cross or a tick as shown in Figure 3.3a.

Figure 3.2 Plotting a point L representing a line of trend 219° and plunge 68° (Example 3.1).

(a)

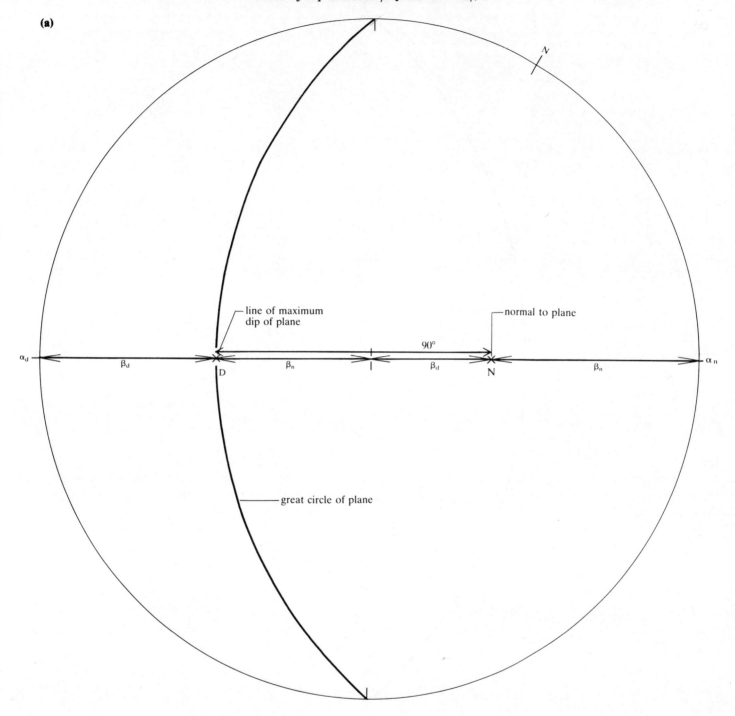

Figure 3.3 Plotting the great circle and the normal to a plane. (a) General method and (b) compass construction of great circle.

The trend α_n and plunge β_n of the normal to the plane are given by

$$\alpha_n = \alpha_d \pm 180° \qquad (0° \leqslant \alpha_n \leqslant 360°)$$
$$\beta_n = 90° - \beta_d$$

The normal to the plane can therefore be plotted in the same way as any other line, using the method described earlier. Alternatively, the normal can be plotted directly

from the α_d and β_d values by simply counting the angle β_d from the centre of the projection along the east–west diameter of the net towards the perimeter diametrically opposite the α_d azimuth, as shown in Figure 3.3a. This automatically ensures that the normal plots 90° from the line of maximum dip, measured across the east–west diameter of the net. It is a good idea at this stage to develop a consistent notation for use on the projections. A recommended system is shown in Figures 3.3 to 3.10.

15

(b)

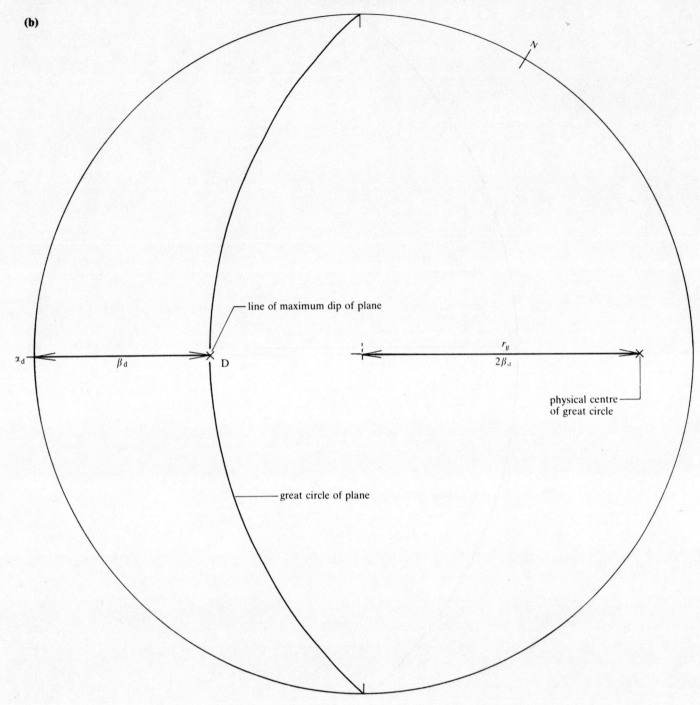

line of maximum dip of plane

$r_{\rm g}$

$2\beta_{\rm d}$

physical centre of great circle

great circle of plane

$\alpha_{\rm d}$

$\beta_{\rm d}$

D

N

Figure 3.3 *Cont.*

It was noted in Section 2.2 that, on an equal-angle projection, the great circle of a plane of dip direction/dip amount $\alpha_{\rm d}/\beta_{\rm d}$ is part of a circular arc that has its centre at a radial distance

$$r_{\rm g} = R \tan \beta_{\rm d}$$

from the centre of the projection measured along a radial line of azimuth $\alpha_{\rm d} \pm 180°$. Comparison with Equation 2.1 shows that the radial distance $r_{\rm g}$ is equivalent to an angular measurement of $2\beta_{\rm d}$ counted from the centre of the projection. This means that, when $\beta_{\rm d}$ is 45° or less, the physical centre of the associated great circle can be located simply by counting the angle $2\beta_{\rm d}$ from the centre of the projection along the radial line of azimuth $\alpha_{\rm d} \pm 180°$. The great circle can then be drawn accurately and rapidly with a pair of compasses set at a radius that takes the circular arc through the line of maximum dip of the plane. This compass construction is illustrated in Figure 3.3b.

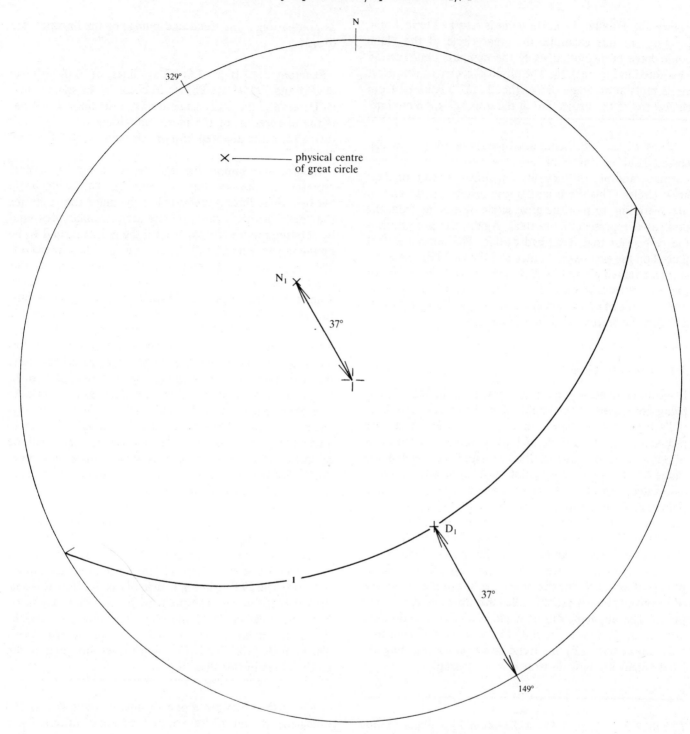

Figure 3.4 Plotting the great circle and normal to a plane of dip direction/dip amount 149/37 (Example 3.2).

Example 3.2 (Fig. 3.4)   Plot the great circle and normal to a plane of dip direction/dip amount 149/37.

The line of maximum dip of the plane in this example has a trend 149° and a plunge 37°. The point D_1 representing this line is first plotted in the usual way. The great circle of the plane is then traced off while this point is still positioned on the east–west diameter of the net. It is, in this case, necessary to trace between the pair of great circles on the net representing planes with dip angles of 36° and 38°. The normal to the plane has a trend 329° and a plunge 53°, and can be plotted in the usual way. Alternatively, the normal can be plotted while the line of maximum dip is still on the east–west diameter of the net by counting the angle of dip of the plane (37°) out from the centre of the net; the resulting point is labelled N_1 in

Figure 3.4. Finally, the north point is returned to its home position. In this example, the great circle of the plane could have been plotted using the compass construction illustrated in Figure 3.3b. The physical centre of this great circle plots at an angle of 74° (i.e. $2 \times 37°$) counted from the centre of the projection in the appropriate direction.

Many of the more complex operations on planes discussed later in this book are best carried out on their normals, and not on their lines of maximum dip or their great circles. This often makes it necessary, at the end of the operation, to plot the great circle of a plane from the point that represents its normal. Again, the procedure is the reverse of that described earlier. The normal is first placed on the east–west diameter of the net. The angle 90° is then counted along this diameter, through the centre of the net, to give, on an ordinary lower-hemisphere projection, the line of maximum dip of the plane. The great circle can then be traced off in the usual way.

3.4 Lines in planes

It has already been noted that a plane can be regarded as being composed of an infinite number of coplanar lines radiating from a single point. On a lower-hemisphere projection the great circle of a plane represents the locus of points generated by such lines with angles of pitch in the range $0° \leqslant \gamma \leqslant 90°$. Any point on a given great circle is associated with a line of some angle of pitch γ, trend α and plunge β. With the strike of the plane on the north–south diameter of the net, the angle of pitch is counted from the perimeter of the net, along the great circle, using the small circles (the 'lines of latitude') on the net as graduations, noting that pitch is always the acute angle. The angle of plunge of any such line that is *not* the line of maximum dip of the given plane is usually called the 'apparent dip' of the plane. The apparent dip of a plane of dip direction/dip amount α_d/β_d ranges from 0° in the strike direction to a value approaching β_d in a trend direction approaching α_d. These ideas are best illustrated using examples.

Example 3.3 (Fig. 3.5) A lineation in a plane of dip direction/dip amount 049/28 has a pitch of 62° measured from the north-west end of the strike line. Find the trend and plunge of the lineation.

The first step is to plot the great circle of the plane 049/28 in the usual way. The north-west end of the strike line of this great circle is located in the north-west quadrant of the net when the north point is at its home position. The great circle is then placed with its strike line on the north–south diameter and the angle 62° is counted along it, from the north-west end, using the small circles

as graduations. The trend and plunge of the lineation are 018/24.

Example 3.4 (Fig. 3.6) Two lines of trend/plunge 204/35 and 273/41 are known to occur in the same plane. (i) Determine the acute angle between the lines. (ii) What is the orientation of the plane containing the two lines? (iii) What is the apparent dip of this plane in the direction 299°?

(i) In this example the first step is to plot the points representing the two lines L_1 and L_2. The acute angle between these lines is measured in the plane that contains the lines. The great circle representing this plane is found by rotating the tracing paper until the points L_1 and L_2 lie on the same great circle of the net, which is then traced off. The angle between L_1 and L_2 is then counted along this great circle, while its strike is still on the north–south diameter of the net, using the small circles as graduations. In this case the angle is 53°; the obtuse angle between the lines is, of course, 127°, which is the supplement of 53°. This pair of supplementary angles is composed of an 'internal angle', measured directly between the points along the great circle, and an 'external angle', measured from L_1 to the perimeter and then from the diametrically opposite side of the perimeter to L_2. This demonstrates an important rule in hemispherical projection: if, when counting an angle along a great circle, it is necessary to cross the perimeter of the net, re-entry is always made at a point diametrically opposite the point of exit and counting continues along the *same* great circle.

(ii) The orientation of the plane containing the two lines is found by reading off the trend and plunge of its line of maximum dip, in this case 248/44.

(iii) The azimuth direction 299° is marked on the perimeter of the projection with the north point at its home position. The 299° azimuth is then placed on the east–west diameter of the net. The point where this diameter intersects the great circle of the plane containing L_1 and L_2 defines the single line in this plane that has a trend 299°. The plunge of this line is 31°, which gives the apparent dip of the plane in this direction.

The angle θ between a pair of lines of trend α_1, α_2 and plunge β_1, β_2 can, if desired, be found algebraically using the following expression

$$\cos \theta = \cos (\alpha_1 - \alpha_2) \cos \beta_1 \cos \beta_2 + \sin \beta_1 \sin \beta_2 \quad (3.1)$$

3.5 Intersecting planes

When two planes intersect they define a line which, by definition, is common to both planes. The trend, plunge and also pitch in each of the planes of this line depends

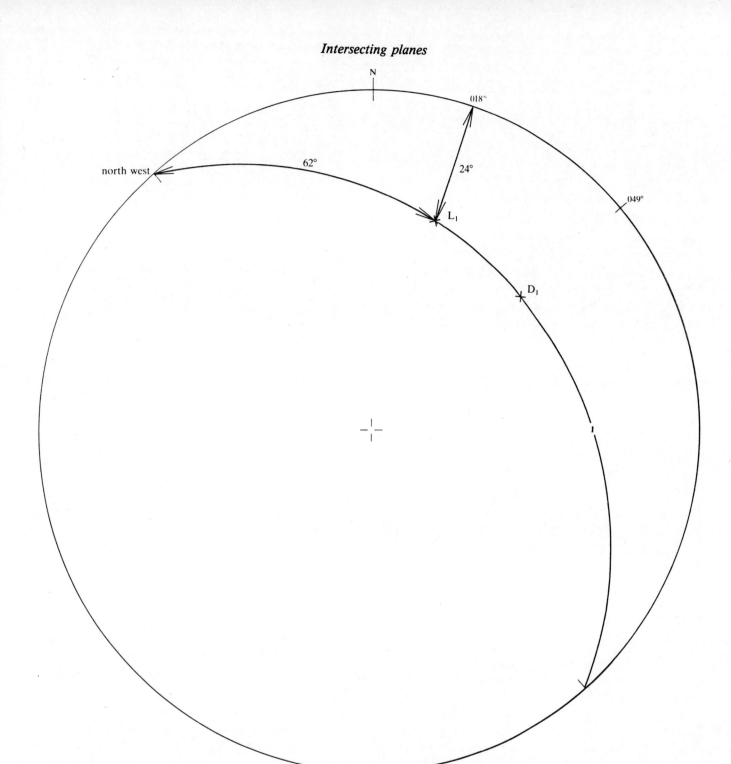

Figure 3.5 Determining the orientation of a line with a pitch of 62° in a plane of dip direction/dip amount 049/28 (Example 3.3).

upon the orientations of the planes involved. On a hemispherical projection, the line of intersection between two planes is represented by the single point defined by the intersection between their great circles. The trend, plunge and pitch of this line of intersection can be read off in the usual way.

Example 3.5 (Fig. 3.7) Plane 1, of dip direction/dip amount 146/59, is intersected by plane 2 of dip direction/dip amount 266/36. Determine the trend and plunge of the line of intersection and its pitch in each of the planes.

The great circles of the two planes, constructed in the usual way, intersect at point I_{12}. This point represents a line with a trend 219°, plunge 26°, a pitch of 31° from the

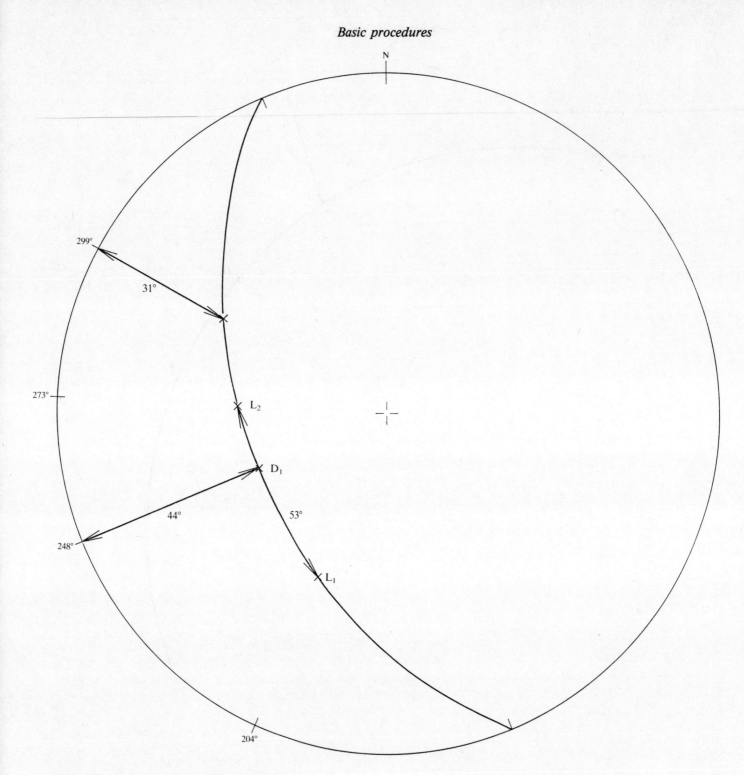

Figure 3.6 Analysis of coplanar lines (Example 3.4).

south-west end of plane 1 and a pitch of 49° from the southern end of plane 2. It is worth noting that the normals to planes 1 and 2 (N_1 and N_2) together lie in a plane that is normal to the line of intersection (I_{12}). This means that I_{12} is the normal to the plane containing N_1 and N_2. In this case, the internal angle between N_1 and N_2, measured in this plane, is 81° as shown in Figure 3.7.

3.6 Rotation about an inclined axis

The orientation of an axis of rotation, like any other line, can be defined in terms of its trend and plunge. It is also necessary, however, to specify the amount and also the direction of the rotation. Consider, for example, a length of core in an inclined borehole, of trend 305° and plunge 65°, containing a discontinuity plane of dip direction/dip

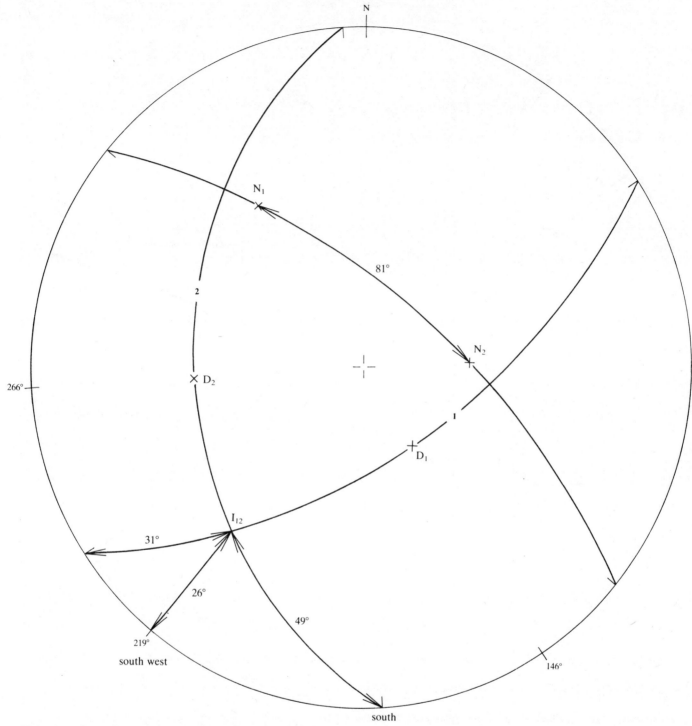

Figure 3.7 The intersection between two planes (Example 3.5).

amount 145/73. If this core is rotated by an amount 55° in a clockwise direction looking down the borehole axis, what will be the new orientation of the discontinuity plane? Problems of this type can be solved rapidly, and with a reasonable degree of accuracy, by using the small circles on the net. These small circles are generated when a plane with a north–south strike, containing a line of constant pitch γ, is rotated about the horizontal north–south diameter of the net. The point, representing a line that is undergoing rotation about the north–south diameter of the net, is therefore moved along the small circle on which it happens to lie, using the great circles on the net as graduations. A clockwise rotation, looking northwards along the north–south diameter of the net, will take the point towards the western side of the net if a lower-hemisphere projection is used; an anticlockwise rotation will take it

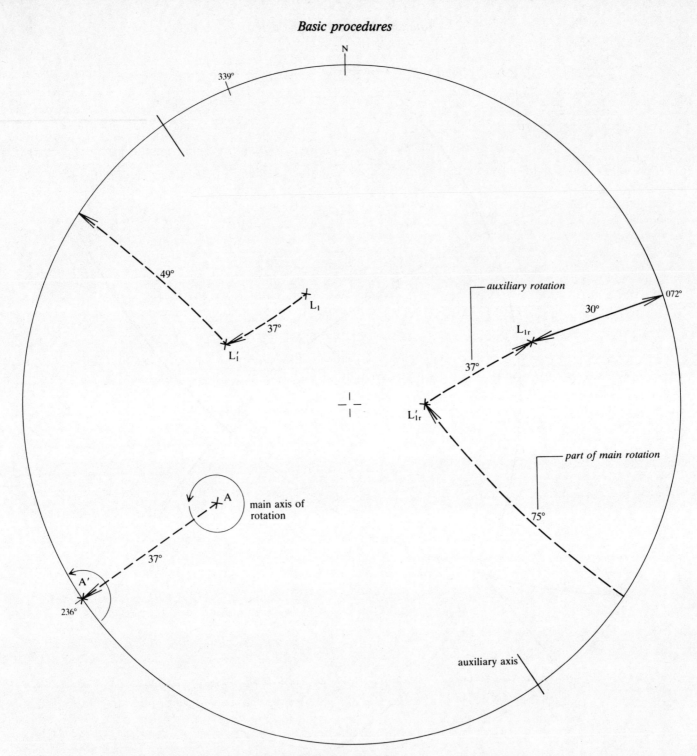

Figure 3.8 Rotation about an inclined axis of trend/plunge 236/37 (Example 3.6).

towards the eastern side. If the point leaves the perimeter of the net, it re-enters at a position diametrically opposite the point of exit, and continues its movement along a small circle. A point leaving the perimeter along a small circle in the southern half of the net will, therefore, re-enter and continue along a geometrically similar small circle in the northern half of the net.

In general the axis of rotation, A, will not be horizontal with a north–south trend, but will have some general trend and plunge α/β. One way of overcoming this complication is to make the axis A *temporarily* coincident with the north–south diameter of the net. This can be achieved by rotating the tracing paper until the axis of rotation, A, lies on the east–west diameter, and then moving the axis along this diameter through the angle β to the perimeter of the net. This operation is, in fact, itself a rotation about an auxiliary axis which is the strike line of the plane for which the axis A is the line of maximum dip. The angle of rotation is the angle of plunge, β, of the axis A; the direction of rotation is towards the trend direction α of the axis A. In order to retain the correct relative geometrical relationships on the projection, all other points must also be rotated about this auxiliary axis, by the same amount and in the same direction. This rotation, in theory, applies for all points, including the centre of the net, which represents the vertical direction. Following this auxiliary rotation, therefore, the projection is effectively constructed in a hemisphere inclined at an angle β from the horizontal. The tracing paper can now be rotated so that the axis A is coincident with the north–south diameter of the net. It is now possible to rotate the points plotted on the net by the prescribed amount and in the prescribed direction. Finally, it is necessary to reverse the auxiliary rotation so that the axis A, and all other points, return to their correct positions on the lower-hemisphere projection.

Example 3.6 (Fig. 3.8) A line of initial trend/plunge 339/51 is rotated about an axis of trend/plunge 236/37 by an amount $124°$ in an anticlockwise direction looking down the axis. What is the resulting orientation of the line?

The first step is to plot the points representing the axis of rotation A and the line L_1. It is helpful, at this stage, to draw a small arrow round the point A indicating the direction of rotation; in this case anticlockwise looking downwards. The point A is then placed on the east–west diameter and moved to the perimeter, through the angle $37°$, to point A'. The direction arrow is similarly translated; the portion of this arrow remaining on the projection gives the direction of movement during the main rotation. The point L_1 is also rotated about the auxiliary axis by the amount $37°$, and in the same direction as point A, along a small circle to point L_1'. The tracing paper is now rotated to bring A' to the north point of the net. The point L_1' can now be rotated through the prescribed angle, $124°$ in this case, by moving it along a small circle in the direction indicated by the arrow near A'. After a rotation of $49°$ the point leaves the perimeter of the net and re-enters, at a position diametrically opposite, to complete the remaining $75°$ of rotation to point L_{1r}'. It is now necessary to reverse the auxiliary rotation by placing A' back on the east–west diameter and moving L_{1r}' along a small circle, in the opposite direction to the initial auxiliary rotation, but through the same angle, $37°$, to point L_{1r}. The new orientation of point L_1, resulting from the rotation, is given by point L_{1r} which has a trend $072°$ and a plunge $30°$. Although the complete operation may seem very lengthy and complicated when explained step by step, it can be carried out in just two or three minutes once the basic principles have been grasped.

The methods explained above can now be applied to the example discussed at the beginning of this section,

concerning the rotation of a length of borehole core containing a discontinuity plane. Although it is theoretically possible to rotate a locus of points representing the great circle of the discontinuity plane, it is much easier to rotate instead the normal to the discontinuity plane and read off the orientation of the rotated plane at the very end. The latter construction, given in Figure 3.9, shows that the rotated discontinuity plane has a dip direction/dip amount 187/58.

If the axis of rotation, A, has a large angle of plunge, it is usually more convenient to rotate this axis to the centre of the projection, rather than to the perimeter, in the auxiliary rotation. As before, during this auxiliary rotation all other points are rotated by the same amount, about the same axis and in the same direction, along small circles, as the axis A. When the auxiliary rotation has been completed, the prescribed main rotation is achieved by swinging the given point through a circular arc, centred on the centre of the projection, through the specified angle and in the specified direction. Finally, the auxiliary rotation is reversed and the orientation of the line is read off. This construction is illustrated in Figure 3.10 using the data in Example 3.6. This alternative method of rotating about an inclined axis, which can be carried out using an equal-angle or an equal-area projection, is particularly valuable in cases where the axis of rotation plunges steeply and/or the angle of rotation is large. Ultimately it is a matter of personal preference in deciding which method is used.

Exercises

3.1 A lineation in a plane of dip direction/dip amount 322/71 has a pitch of $55°$ measured from the south-west end of the strike line. Find the trend and plunge of the lineation.

3.2 Two lines of trend/plunge 124/68 and 227/32 are known to be coplanar. (i) Determine the obtuse angle between the lines. (ii) What is the trend and plunge of the line that bisects the obtuse angle between the two lines? (iii) What is the orientation of the plane containing the two lines? (iv) What is the apparent dip of this plane in the direction $197°$?

3.3 The line of intersection between two planes has a plunge of $38°$ and a trend in the north-west quadrant. If the first plane has a dip direction/dip amount 256/50, what is the trend direction of the line of intersection? It is known that the second plane has a strike of $132°$; what is the angle of dip of the second plane?

3.4 A length of core, from a borehole with an axis of trend/plunge 143/68, contains a discontinuity plane of dip direction/dip amount 204/47. It is known that the core has rotated through a clockwise angle (looking down the axis) of $140°$ during retrieval from the hole. What will be the apparent dip direction/dip amount of the discontinuity plane as the core emerges from the borehole?

Answers to these exercises are given on page 123.

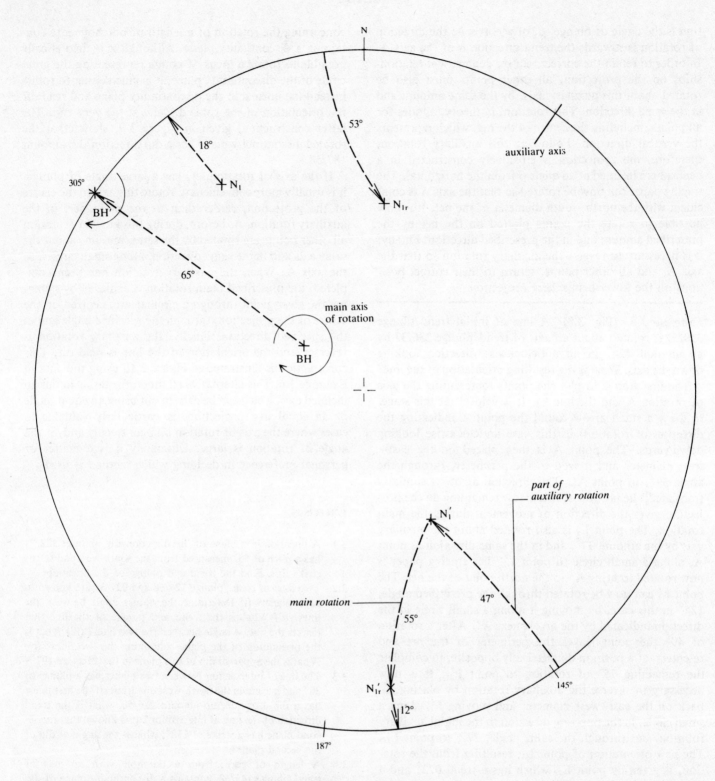

Figure 3.9 Rotation about a borehole axis of trend/plunge 305/65.

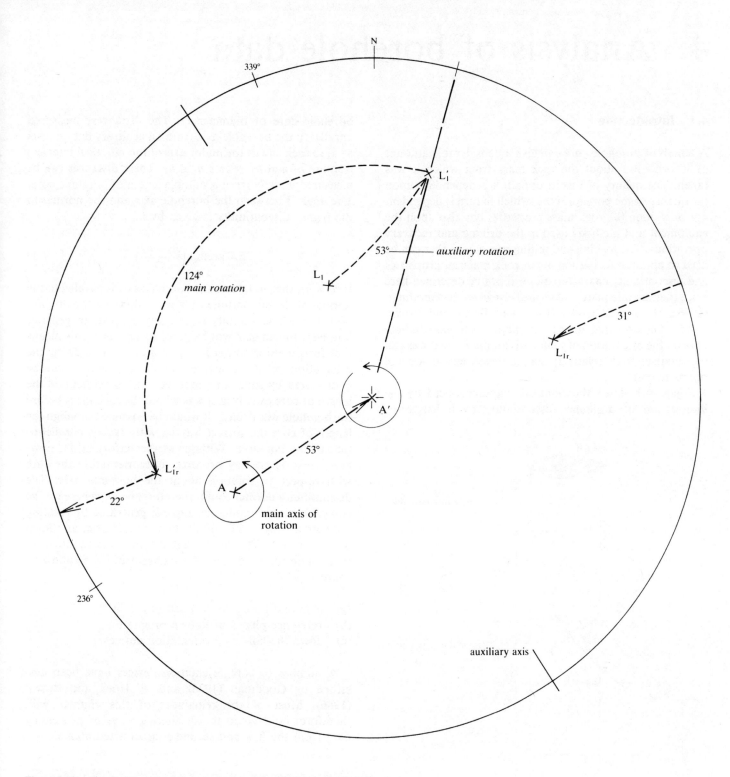

Figure 3.10 Alternative method for rotation about an inclined axis (Example 3.6).

4 Analysis of borehole data

4.1 Introduction

A length of borehole core can give a considerable amount of information about the rock mass from which it was taken. The quality of this information is dependent upon the quality of the borehole core, which in turn is dependent not only upon the rock mass properties but also upon the equipment and methods used in the drilling and recovery operations. The logging and testing procedures that can be used to obtain information about rock material properties and discontinuity characteristics will not be described here since they are adequately described elsewhere by Goodman (1976), Hoek and Brown (1980) and Brady and Brown (1985). The principal aim of this chapter is to explain how data on the orientation of planar discontinuity features can be obtained from relatively simple measurements on the borehole core.

Figure 4.1 shows the elliptical shape produced by the intersection of a planar discontinuity by a length of

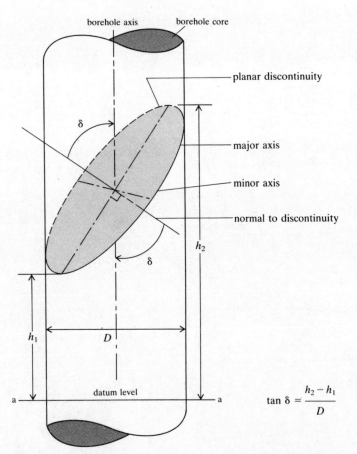

Figure 4.1 The intersection between a planar discontinuity and a length of borehole core.

$$\tan \delta = \frac{h_2 - h_1}{D}$$

borehole core of diameter D. The distances, measured parallel to the borehole axis from an arbitrary datum level a–a, to each end of the major axis of this elliptical intersection are h_1 and h_2, where $h_1 \leqslant h_2$. These distances can be measured directly from a suitable length of borehole core. The angle δ between the borehole axis and the normal to the planar discontinuity is given by

$$\delta = \arctan\left(\frac{h_2 - h_1}{D}\right) \qquad (4.1)$$

If $h_1 = h_2$, then $\delta = 0$ and the borehole axis is parallel to the normal of the discontinuity plane. In this case the orientation of the discontinuity is uniquely defined. In general, however, the angle δ will be greater than zero; this means that further information is required in order to define the orientation of the discontinuity. This problem can be appreciated by supposing that we wish to reorientate the length of core exactly as it was within the rock mass before the borehole was drilled. It would be possible to realign the length of core the correct way up with its axis parallel to that of the borehole. Without further information, however, there is no way of correctly reorientating the core with respect to rotation about the borehole axis. The discontinuity normal could, therefore, lie anywhere on the conical locus, of semi-apex angle δ, generated by rotating the core through $360°$ about the borehole axis, as shown in Figure 4.2. The additional information required to reorientate the core can be obtained from the following sources:

(a) a second borehole, inclined to the first;
(b) reference planes of known orientation;
(c) down-the-hole core orientation devices.

A number of core orientation devices have been described by Goodman (1976) and by Hoek and Brown (1980). Most of the remainder of this chapter will, therefore, be devoted to considering ways of processing data from the first and second sources listed above.

4.2 Construction of the locus defined by a cone angle δ about an axis of trend/plunge α/β

The locus of possible true orientations of the discontinuity normal, illustrated in Figure 4.2, can be represented on a lower-hemisphere projection. This locus, which is in fact a small circle, can be constructed using either a general

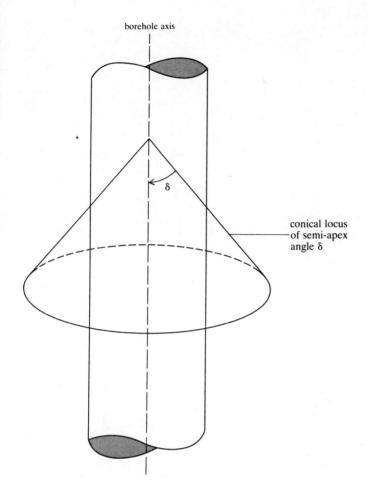

borehole axis

conical locus
of semi-apex
angle δ

δ

Figure 4.2 Conical locus, giving the possible true orientations of the discontinuity normal.

method, suitable for equal-area and equal-angle projections, or alternatively by a quicker and more accurate compass construction, suitable only for equal-angle projections.

4.2.1 General method

The first step is to plot the point L representing the line, of trend/plunge α/β, about which the cone angle is to be constructed. The point L is then placed on any convenient great circle. The cone angle δ can now be counted along the great circle, in both directions from L, to define a pair of points on the required locus. If, during counting, it is necessary to cross the perimeter of the net, counting is continued along the *same* great circle, from a point 180° diametrically opposite the point of exit. The required locus is gradually built up by placing the point L on a range of different great circles to generate several pairs of points at the required angle δ from L. The resulting locus, when plotted on an equal-angle projection, is circular in shape. On an equal-area projection the locus takes the shape of a fourth-order curve.

4.2.2 Compass construction

On an equal-angle projection, the locus defined by a cone angle δ about a line of trend/plunge α/β is composed of a complete or part circular arc with a radius R_s given by Equation 2.5, which can be expressed as follows

$$R_s = R(A - B)/2 \qquad (4.2)$$

where R is the radius of the projection,

$$A = \tan\left(\frac{90 - \beta + \delta}{2}\right) \qquad B = \tan\left(\frac{90 - \beta - \delta}{2}\right)$$

and $\delta < 90° + \beta$. The circular arc has its centre, c, at a trend α; however, unless $\beta = 90°$ the point c does not coincide with the point L which represents the line of trend/plunge α/β. By applying Equations 2.1 and 4.2 it can be shown that the true centre, c, of the circular arc lies at a radial distance r_c from the centre of the projection given by

$$r_c = R(A + B)/2 \qquad (4.3)$$

As before, the first step in plotting the circular arc is to plot the point L representing the line of trend/plunge α/β. The point L is then placed on the east–west diameter of the net, and the cone angle δ is counted along this diameter in both directions from L. The two resulting points lie on diametrically opposite sides of the circular locus, of cone angle δ. The diameter of the locus is given by the physical distance between these points. The true centre of the locus, which lies halfway between these points can, alternatively, be located using Equation 4.3. The locus can now be constructed with a pair of compasses.

If the angle δ is greater than β, part of the locus will extend beyond the perimeter of the projection. In such a case it will only be possible to plot one point on the east–west diameter, at a cone angle δ from L measured towards, and perhaps through, the centre of the net. It will therefore be necessary to use Equation 4.2 to calculate the radius R_s of the circular arc. The part of the circular arc surrounding the point L can then be constructed using a pair of compasses as described above. The remainder of the circular arc plots on the diametrically opposite side of the projection and, since it does not have a radius R_s, is best plotted using the general method outlined earlier.

Example 4.1 (Figs 4.3 & 4.4). Construct the loci defined by (1) a cone angle of 60° about an axis of trend/plunge 130/70 and (2) a cone angle of 50° about an axis of trend/plunge 044/10.

Figure 4.3 shows the general method of locus construction applied to this example. The points L_1 and L_2, which represent the axes of the required cones, are plotted in the

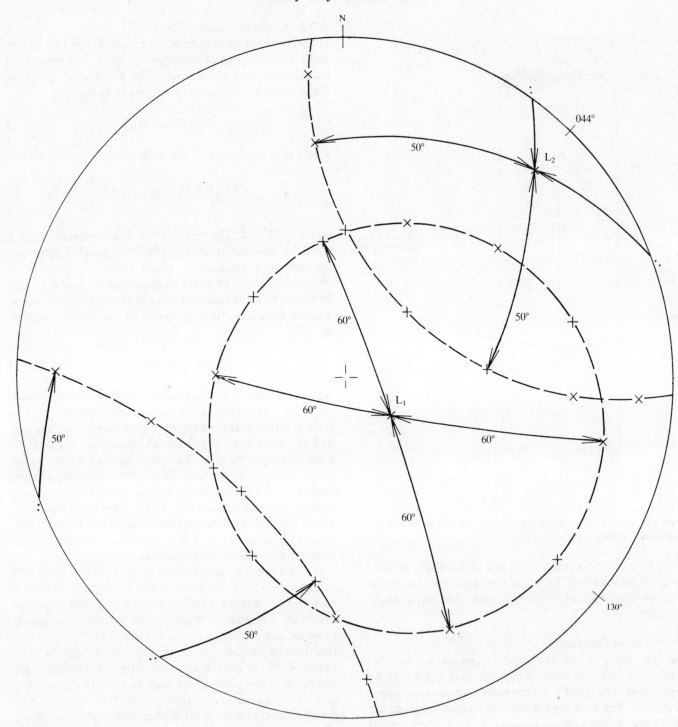

Figure 4.3 Construction of circular loci using the general method (Example 4.1).

usual way. The point L_1 is then placed on a convenient great circle and the cone angle of 60° is counted off in both directions along this great circle. This is repeated several times to generate sufficient points to permit a reasonably accurate interpolation of the circular locus. This process is repeated for the 50° cone angle measured from L_2. In some cases, when measuring from L_2, it is necessary to cross the perimeter of the net and continue counting along the same

great circle from a point diametrically opposite to the point of exit. It is worth noting that the two separate parts of the locus about L_2 have different radii.

Figure 4.4 shows the compass construction method applied to this example. The points L_1 and L_2 are plotted as before. With L_1 on the east–west diameter of the net, the cone angle of 60° is counted in both directions along this diameter to give two points L'_1 and L''_1, which are at

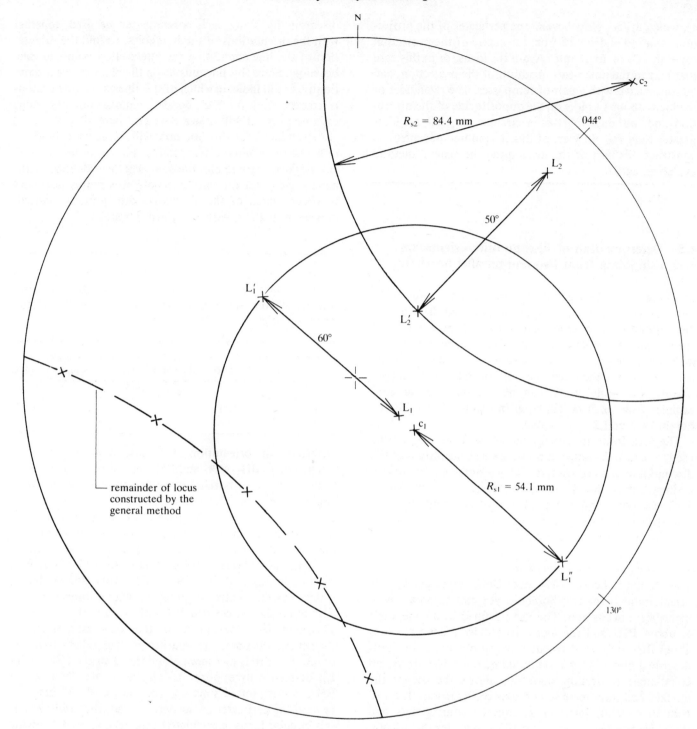

Figure 4.4 Construction of circular loci using the compass construction method (Example 4.1).

opposite ends of one diameter of the required circular locus. The physical centre of this locus, c_1, is therefore midway between these points, giving a radius R_{s1} of approximately 54 mm. Alternatively, and more precisely, Equations 4.2 and 4.3 give R_{s1} and r_{c1} as 54.1 mm and 21.4 mm respectively for a projection of 90 mm radius. The locus can be constructed with a pair of compasses. The point L_2 is next placed on the east–west diameter of the

net, and the point L_2' is marked at an angular separation of 50° from L_2 measured along this diameter. The diametrically opposite point L_2'' cannot be plotted because the cone angle of 50° places it beyond the perimeter of the projection. In this case, therefore, the radius of the locus R_{s2} must be obtained using Equation 4.2. The resulting value of 84.4 mm for the 90 mm projection is measured from L_2' through L_2 to give the physical centre of the locus

c_2, which in fact plots beyond the perimeter of the projection, at a radial distance from the centre of the projection (by Eqn 4.3) of 108.6 mm. Again the locus, or in this case that part in the north-east quadrant of the projection, can be constructed with a pair of compasses. The remainder of the locus about L_2 plots on the opposite side of the projection and, although part of a circular arc, has a radius greater than R_{s2}. In view of this it is more convenient to construct this part of the locus using the general method explained earlier.

4.3 Determination of discontinuity orientation using data from two non-parallel boreholes

Boreholes 1 and 2, which are not parallel, are assumed to intersect the same set of recognisable, parallel, planar discontinuities. The trends and plunges of these boreholes are assumed to be known, and to have the values α_{b1}/β_{b1} and α_{b2}/β_{b2} respectively. It is also assumed that the angle between the borehole axis and the normal to the recognisable discontinuity set can be measured using core samples from each borehole, giving values δ_1 and δ_2 for boreholes 1 and 2 respectively.

The data from these two non-parallel boreholes can be used to reduce the range of possible true orientations of the discontinuity normal from the infinite number of values on a single conical locus to, in most cases, just two values. There are two commonly used ways of achieving this on a hemispherical projection: (i) the full small-circle method, and (ii) the half small-circle method.

4.3.1 Full small-circle method
The points labelled BH_1 and BH_2, representing the orientations of the two boreholes are plotted on a lower-hemisphere projection. The locus defined by a cone angle δ_1 about BH_1 and the locus defined by a cone angle δ_2 about BH_2 are then constructed using one of the methods described above. It is usually more convenient to use an equal-angle projection since this allows the use of the quicker and more precise compass construction. The loci will, in general, intersect at two, or four, points and therefore give two, or four, possible values for the orientation of the normal to the discontinuity set. If the loci do not intersect or touch, then the input data are in error.

Additional information required to decide which orientation is the correct one may be available from the following three different sources. (i) There may be some information about the approximate true angle of dip of the set, which would differentiate between two alternatives of widely differing orientations. (ii) One particular discontinuity may be recognisable in core from both boreholes. When this happens, the intersection distances of the

discontinuity along each borehole can be used, together with the orientations of the boreholes, to find the orientation of the line connecting the intersection points in each borehole. Since this line must lie in the plane of the discontinuity, it will indicate which of the alternative orientations is correct. (iii) A third borehole intersecting the same discontinuity set will indicate which orientation is correct since the locus for this borehole will, in general, intersect only one of the alternatives produced by the other two loci. It is not necessary to plot the complete locus defined by the cone angle δ_3 for the third borehole; it is simply necessary to check which of the alternative discontinuity normals makes an angle δ_3 with this third borehole.

Example 4.2 (Fig. 4.5) The following data were obtained from three non-parallel boreholes, each of which intersected the same distinctive set of parallel planar discontinuities:

Borehole	Trend (deg)	Plunge (deg)	Angle between borehole axis and the normal to the discontinuity set (deg)
1	049	71	59
2	127	20	43
3	223	40	67

Determine the orientation of the discontinuity set.

The points BH_1, BH_2 and BH_3 representing the orientations of the three boreholes are first plotted on an equal-angle projection. The point BH_1 is then placed on the east–west diameter of the net and two points, L_1' and L_1'', are marked at an angular separation of $59°$ from BH_1 measured along this diameter. The points L_1' and L_1'' are on opposite ends of one diameter of the circular locus defined by a cone angle of $59°$ about BH_1. This circular locus, which has its centre at point c_1 and a radius R_{s1} of 52.8 mm, can be constructed with a pair of compasses. The point BH_2 is next placed on the east–west diameter of the net and the point L_2' is marked at an angular separation of $43°$ from BH_2 measured along this diameter. The point L_2'', diametrically opposite L_2' on the circular locus about BH_2, is not plotted since the cone angle of $43°$ places it beyond the perimeter of the net. Instead, the radius R_{s2} of this circular locus is calculated using Equation 4.2, giving a value of 57.2 mm. The part of the circular locus about BH_2, which has its centre at a distance R_{s2} from L_2', can now be plotted using compasses. The remainder of this locus is plotted using the general construction method. If preferred, the centres and radii of the circular loci can be determined from Equations 4.2 and 4.3, thereby obviating the need to plot any points on the perimeter of each locus.

The circular loci about BH_1 and BH_2 intersect at two points, N_1 and N_2, which give two possible orientations of the normal to the discontinuity set intersecting the bore-

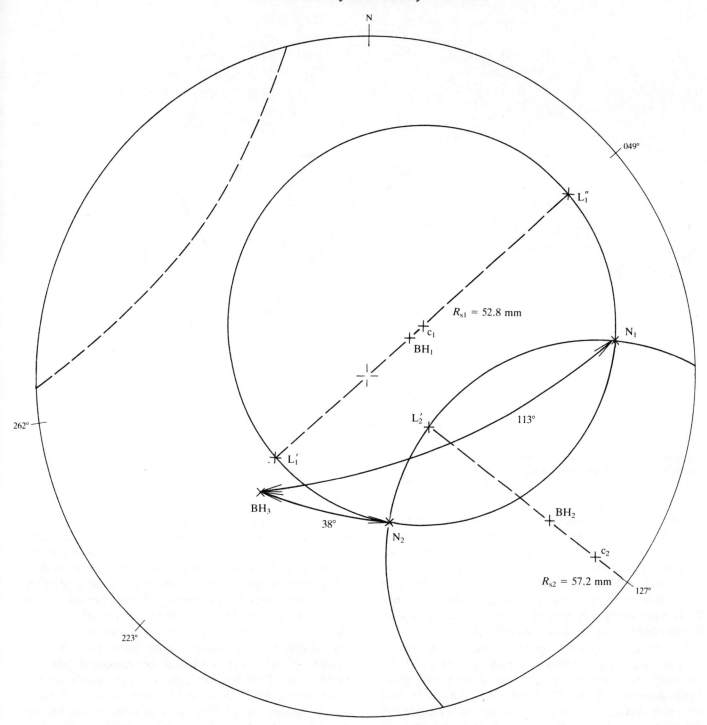

Figure 4.5 Analysis of data from non-parallel boreholes using the full small-circle method (Example 4.2).

holes. The angle between BH_3 and N_1 is 113° measured internally and 67° measured externally; the corresponding angles for N_2 are 38° and 142°. The acute angle of 67° agrees with the measured value for borehole 3 and confirms that N_1 represents the correct orientation. The trend/plunge of this normal are 082/15, giving the dip direction/dip amount of the set as 262/75.

It is worth commenting upon the general symmetry in the relative orientations of the two non-parallel boreholes and the two possible orientations N_1 and N_2. This symmetry arises from the three-dimensional geometry of the two mutually intersecting conical loci which have a common apex. The plane containing the two borehole axes is here referred to as plane B; the plane containing the two possible orientations N_1 and N_2 is referred to as plane C.

31

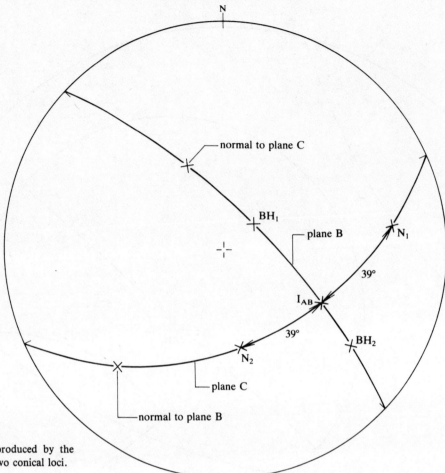

Figure 4.6 Symmetry produced by the mutual intersection of two conical loci.

The normal to plane B always lies in plane C. Similarly the normal to plane C always lies in plane B. In other words, plane C is at right angles to plane B. Moreover, the points N_1 and N_2 are symmetrically disposed about plane B. In this particular example N_1 and N_2 each make an angle of approximately $39°$ with plane B, measured along the plane C. This symmetry is illustrated in Figure 4.6 using the data for boreholes 1 and 2 from Example 4.2.

It is necessary to use the 'general method' for constructing cone angle loci on equal-area projections, and also for the portions of loci that extend beyond the perimeter on equal-angle projections. This general method can be both time-consuming and, unless care is taken, rather imprecise. The half small-circle method offers an alternative way of analysing data from two non-parallel boreholes.

4.3.2 Half small-circle method

This method utilises the small circles of the net. These small circles represent loci constructed about a horizontal north–south axis. The cone angle for a particular small circle is given by the angle of pitch associated with that small circle. In order to utilise these small circles it is necessary to carry out an auxiliary rotation to make each borehole temporarily horizontal and aligned along the

north–south diameter of the net. This is most easily achieved by placing the two boreholes on their common great circle and then rotating them to the horizontal about the north–south diameter of the net. This axis of rotation corresponds to the strike direction of the plane containing the two boreholes. Each, now horizontal, borehole is then placed, in turn, on the north–south diameter of the net so that the small circle, with a pitch angle corresponding to the appropriate cone angle, can be traced from the net. Each small circle is in two halves: one measured from the north point of the net, the other from the south point.

As before, the small circles for two boreholes will intersect to define two or four possible orientations for the normal to the discontinuity set. It is first necessary, however, to reverse the auxiliary rotation, described above, before attempting to read off the possible orientations of the discontinuity set. Data from a third borehole can be used, as described in the previous section, to decide which of the possible orientations is the correct one.

Figure 4.7 illustrates the half small-circle method using the data in Example 4.2. An auxiliary rotation is first carried out to make *one* pair of the three boreholes BH_1, BH_2 and BH_3 temporarily horizontal. In this case, boreholes 2 and 3 have been selected, requiring a rotation

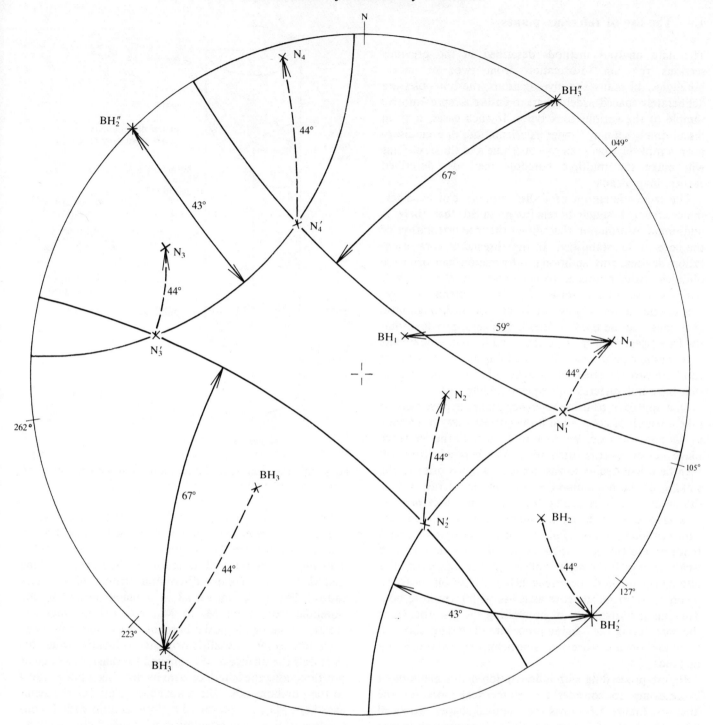

Figure 4.7 Analysis of data from non-parallel boreholes using the half small-circle method (Example 4.2).

of 44° about the horizontal axis of trend 105°. This gives points BH$'_2$ and BH$'_3$ on the perimeter of the projection; the points BH$''_2$ and BH$''_3$ are then marked diametrically opposite to the points BH$'_2$ and BH$'_3$ respectively. The points BH$'_2$ and BH$''_2$ can now be placed on the north–south diameter of the net so that the small circle corresponding to the cone angle of 43° can be traced off in two halves. This process is repeated for a cone angle of 67° measured

from BH$'_3$ and BH$''_3$. The small circles for boreholes 2 and 3 intersect at four points: N$'_1$ to N$'_4$. The true orientations of these points are found by reversing the auxiliary rotation of 44° about the axis 105° to give the points N$_1$ to N$_4$. These four points make acute angles of 59°, 24°, 76° and 79° with BH$_1$. This shows that N$_1$ is the correct orientation of the discontinuity normal, giving, as before, the dip direction/dip amount of the set as 262/75.

4.4 The use of reference planes

The data analysis methods described in the previous sections rely on information from two, or more, boreholes. In many site investigations, the boreholes are deliberately spaced widely apart to ensure a representative sample of the various rock types. In such cases, a given discontinuity set may change its orientation, or even disappear completely, between one borehole and the next. This will make the multiple borehole methods, described earlier, inapplicable.

The true orientation of a discontinuity can be determined from a single borehole, provided that there is additional information that allows the true orientation of the core to be established. In the absence of core orientation devices, this additional information can often be obtained from reference planes present in the borehole core. Any set of recognisable, persistent planar features whose orientation is known to be consistent throughout a rock mass can be used as reference planes, provided that the true orientation can be established from measurements in a borehole or at a rock face. Bedding and slaty cleavage can both provide excellent reference planes in rock masses that have not suffered subsequent folding.

One approach to using reference planes is physically to take a length of core, align it the correct way up, parallel to the borehole axis, and then rotate it until the reference plane lies at its true orientation. The borehole core will then be orientated as it was in the rock mass prior to the sinking of the borehole. The orientations of the various discontinuities intersecting the core can, therefore, be measured directly using a suitable compass-clinometer. This method becomes impracticable if the length of core is rendered too fragile by the presence of discontinuities and weak zones or if the marker planes are widely spaced. The alternative method, described below, relies on measurements taken from the core as it lies within the core box. This has the advantage of minimising the disturbance of the core during the logging procedure. The data obtained from the core are processed using hemispherical projection methods.

Before proceeding with a description of the methods, it is necessary to consider the geometrical basis for the analysis. Figure 4.8 shows the elliptical shapes produced where a length of borehole core is intersected by planar features whose normals are not parallel to the borehole axis. The minor axis of each ellipse generated by a given planar feature is always a diameter of the borehole, and hence is normal to the borehole axis. This minor axis is also, by definition, normal to the major axis of the ellipse. Both the minor and major axes of the ellipse are parallel to the given planar feature and hence make an angle of 90° with the normal to this plane. It follows, therefore, that the borehole axis, the major axis of the ellipse and the normal to the given planar feature are coplanar since each

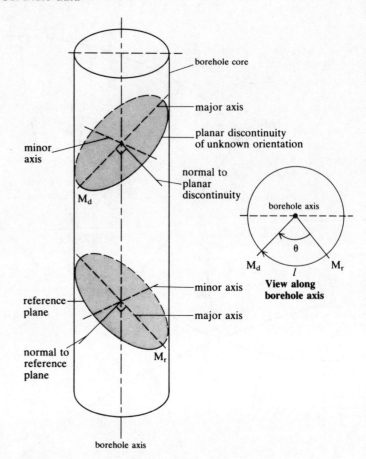

Figure 4.8 The geometrical basis for the use of reference planes in the analysis of borehole data.

is normal to the minor axis of the ellipse. The major semi-axis furthest from the borehole collar will be used as an important reference line in the analysis described below. This line will be referred to as M_r for the reference plane and M_d for a given planar discontinuity of unknown orientation. The angle, measured in a plane normal to the borehole axis, from M_r to M_d, counted in clockwise rotation looking along the borehole drive direction, is θ.

In practice, it is usually fairly easy to identify where M_r intersects the surface of the core and to transfer its angular position along the length of core by drawing a line parallel to the borehole axis. The analogous points for the semi-axes M_{d1}, M_{d2}, ... produced by intersections with discontinuities of unknown orientation can similarly be identified and marked on the surface of the core. Each angle θ can be determined by measuring the physical distance l round the perimeter of the core from M_r to M_d. The angle θ in degrees, is given by

$$\theta = 360l/\pi D$$

where D is the diameter of the core. The various angles δ_1, δ_2, ... between the normal to each discontinuity plane and the borehole axis can be measured using the method

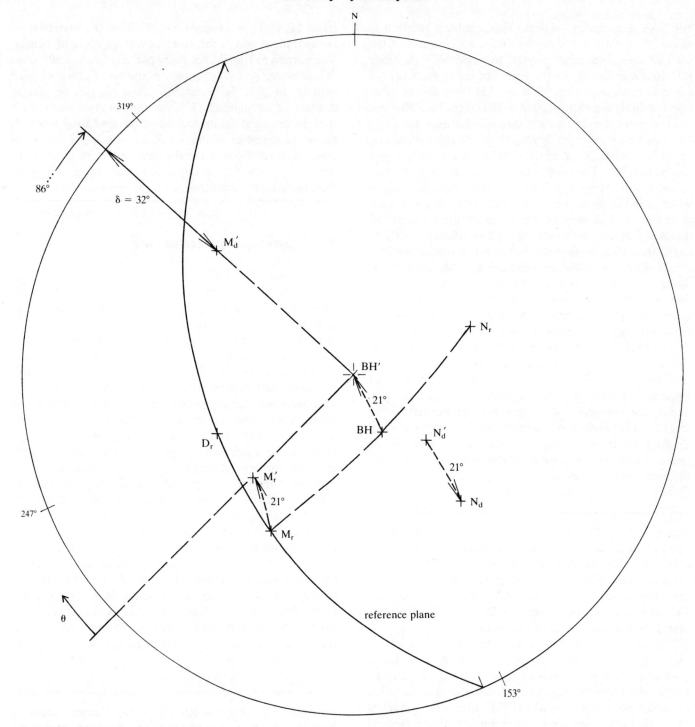

Figure 4.9 The use of a reference plane in the analysis of borehole data (Example 4.3).

described earlier and illustrated in Figure 4.1. The remaining input data required are the trend and plunge of the borehole, α_b and β_b, and the dip direction and dip amount of the reference plane, α_{dr} and β_{dr}. It is assumed that these orientations are known.

The first step in the analysis is to plot on a lower hemisphere projection the point BH, representing the borehole axis of trend/plunge α_b/β_b. The great circle and

normal, N_r, of the reference plane of known dip direction/dip amount α_{dr}/β_{dr} are also plotted. The point M_r, representing the major axis of the elliptical intersection between the borehole core and the reference plane, lies on the great circle of the reference plane at a point that places it in the same plane as (i.e. on the great circle containing) BH and N_r. The point M_r can now be plotted. The subsequent analysis is best carried out by first making the borehole temporarily vertical. This auxiliary rotation is achieved by placing BH on the east–west diameter of the net and then rotating it through an angle $90° - \beta_b$ along this diameter directly to the centre of the projection. (In the rare cases where the borehole has been driven in an upward direction, this rotation to the centre is carried out via the perimeter of the net through the external angle $90° + \beta_b$.) The point M_r is rotated in the same direction, about the same axis and by the same amount as BH, to give the point M_r'. The perimeter of the projection now represents the plane that is normal to the borehole axis in which the angle θ was measured. The angle θ can, therefore, be counted in clockwise rotation round the perimeter of the net from the radius containing M_r' to define the radius containing M_d', the major semi-axis of the discontinuity of unknown orientation. The point M_d' is plotted at an angle δ measured along this radius, from the perimeter of the net, as if it were an angle of plunge. The normal to the discontinuity, N_d', plots at an angle of $90°$ from M_d' measured in the plane containing the borehole axis and M_d'. This plane is represented by a diameter of the net since the borehole axis is at the centre of the projection. The true orientation of the discontinuity can now be obtained by reversing the auxiliary rotation, described above, for the point N_d' to give N_d, the normal to the discontinuity plane. It is possible to analyse several discontinuities on a single diagram since all of them will be related to the same reference plane and, hence, undergo the same auxiliary rotation.

Example 4.3 (Fig. 4.9) A length of core from a borehole, of trend/plunge 153/69, is intersected by a reference plane of dip direction/dip amount 247/41. Angular measurements taken from the elliptical shape produced by the intersection of a planar discontinuity with the core yielded the following values: $\theta = 86°$, $\delta = 32°$. Find the orientation of the discontinuity plane.

The first step is to plot the available data: the borehole axis BH, the normal to the reference plane N_r and also its great circle. The great circle containing N_r and BH can now be traced off and its intersection with the great circle of the reference plane can be marked. This intersection, labelled M_r in Figure 4.9, represents the major axis of the elliptical intersection between the borehole core and the reference plane.

The auxiliary rotation is achieved by placing BH on the east–west diameter and then moving it to the centre of the net through the angle $21°$. The point M_r, which is rotated about the same axis as BH, is moved $21°$ along a small circle to the point M_r'. The angle θ, of $86°$, is measured in clockwise rotation from the radius containing M_r' to define the radius containing M_d'. This latter point represents the major axis of the ellipse for the discontinuity plane. The

point M_d' plots at an angle $\delta = 32°$ from the perimeter of the net, measured in the same way as an angle of plunge. The normal to the discontinuity plane, N_d', plots $90°$ from M_d' measured across a diameter of the net. There is no need actually to plot the point M_d', since N_d' can be plotted directly, at an angle of $32°$ from the borehole axis (which is at the centre of the projection), measured away from M_d' along the diameter of the net containing M_d'. Finally, the point N_d' is recovered from the auxiliary rotation of $21°$ to define N_d, the normal of the discontinuity plane. This gives the dip direction/dip amount of the plane as 319/52.

4.5 Analysis of orientated core

The method described above can be used, with minor modifications, to process data obtained from core that has been orientated using some down-the-hole mechanical or electrical device. The most convenient way to utilise the information obtained from such a device is to construct a linear reference mark, parallel to the borehole axis, along the surface of the core. The circumferential position of this reference mark is defined by the orientation of an arbitrary imaginary line, L_r, constructed in the plane normal to the borehole axis from the centre of the core to the reference mark. In a vertical borehole L_r would usually be the north direction, in which case the reference mark would simply give the northern azimuth on the core perimeter. In an inclined borehole, L_r would usually be the line of maximum dip of the plane normal to the borehole axis. In this case the reference mark would be the 'bottom point' of the core, in other words the line that would be traced by a ball-bearing free to roll down the borehole.

During data analysis, the line L_r can be used in exactly the same way as the line M_r referred to earlier. In particular, the angle θ can be measured from the reference mark, defined by L_r, to M_d as illustrated in Figure 4.8. The method of analysis, which is basically the same as that described earlier, is best explained using a simple example.

Example 4.4 (Fig. 4.10) A core sample from a borehole, of trend/plunge 293/55, carries a reference mark constructed at the 'bottom point' of the core. Angular measurements taken from the elliptical shape produced by the intersection of a planar discontinuity with the core yielded the following values: $\theta = 237°$, $\delta = 49°$. Find the orientation of the discontinuity plane.

As before, the first step is to plot the borehole axis, BH, and the line of maximum dip, L_r, of the plane normal to the borehole axis. The auxiliary rotation of $35°$ takes BH to the centre of the projection, while the point L_r moves to L_r' on the perimeter of the projection. The angle θ of $237°$

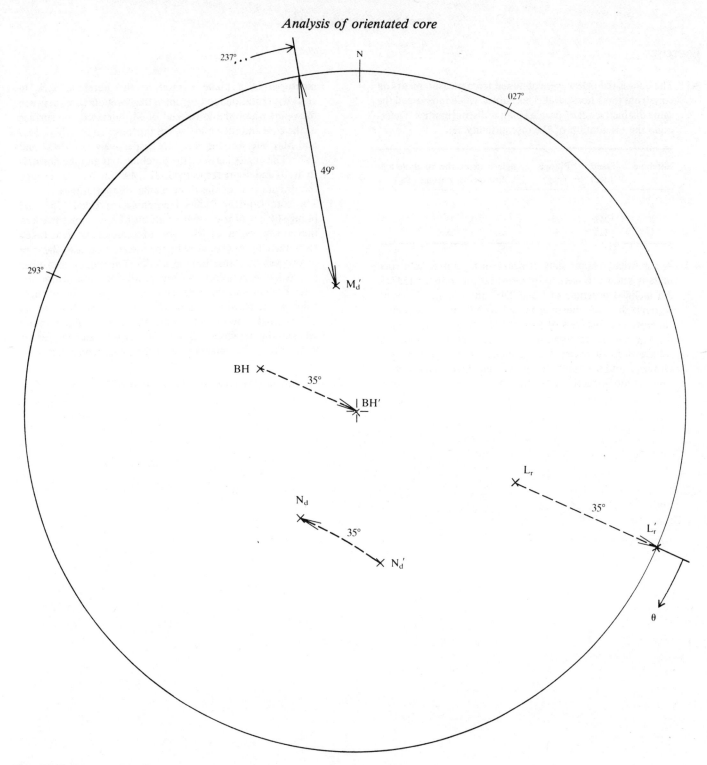

Figure 4.10 The use of a reference mark in the analysis of borehole data (Example 4.4).

is counted in clockwise rotation from L_r' to define the radius containing M_d'. Again, M_d' plots at an angle δ (in this case 49°) from the perimeter of the projection and the normal to the discontinuity plane, N_d', plots 90° from M_d'. Finally, N_d' is recovered from the auxiliary rotation of 35° to point N_d, which gives the dip direction/dip amount of the discontinuity plane as 027/40.

Exercises

4.1 The data listed below were obtained from measurements on core from three non-parallel boreholes which intersected the same distinctive set of parallel planar discontinuities. Determine the orientation of the discontinuity set.

Borehole	Trend (deg)	Plunge (deg)	Angle between the borehole axis and the set normal (deg)
1	143	65	47
2	251	28	34
3	324	60	28

4.2 A persistent, planar slaty cleavage in a jointed slate rock mass is known to have a dip direction/dip amount 158/25. An inclined borehole of trend 230° and plunge 75°, sunk through the rock mass, produced core samples containing three well defined sets of planar discontinuities, d_1, d_2 and d_3. The lines representing the major axes of the elliptical intersections between the borehole core and the slaty cleavage, and the borehole core and the three planar discontinuities are respectively M_r, M_{d1}, M_{d2} and M_{d3}. The angles, measured in a plane normal to the borehole axis, in clockwise rotation looking down the borehole core, between the point where the lower end of M_r intersects the surface of the core and the points where the lower ends of M_{d1}, M_{d2} and M_{d3} intersect the core, are respectively 16°, 143° and 287°. The angles between the borehole axis and the normals to d_1, d_2 and d_3 are respectively 32°, 49° and 68°. Determine the orientations of the three planar discontinuities.

4.3 The core from an inclined borehole, of trend 128° and plunge 66°, was orientated by means of a reference mark at the bottom point of the core. Measurements were taken from the ellipses produced by the intersection with the core of two sets of planar discontinuities. The angles, measured in clockwise rotation looking down the core, from the reference mark to the lower ends of the major axes of these elliptical intersections, were 116° for set 1 and 219° for set 2. The angles between the normals of these discontinuity sets and the borehole axis were 74° for set 1 and 51° for set 2. Determine the orientations of the two discontinuity sets.

Answers to these exercises are given on page 123.

5 Statistical analysis of orientation data

5.1 Introduction

The orientation of discontinuities in a rock mass can be determined using the borehole methods explained in Chapter 4 or, alternatively, measured at an exposed rock face either above or below ground. It is generally desirable to take several hundred orientation measurements at a given location, to permit the use of statistical analysis. In view of this, it is important that the sampling process is as objective as possible. For a length of borehole core this can be achieved by measuring all the discontinuities that intersect the core. At a rock face it is now common practice to impose a similar linear sampling regime by measuring all the discontinuities that intersect a sampling line or 'scanline' set up on the rock face. This scanline is usually a standard measuring tape fixed vertically or horizontally

to the rock face. The discontinuity orientation data, obtained either from a borehole or from a rock face, can be presented graphically on a hemispherical projection. The simplest way to do this is to plot points representing the normals to each of the discontinuity planes measured. It may even be feasible to use symbols of different shapes to represent different types of discontinuities (joints, bedding planes, faults, etc.) and to use different sizes of symbols to represent the range of discontinuity sizes. An example of such a plot is shown in Figure 5.1. Diagrams of this type have great visual impact and provide valuable assistance when trying to understand the structure of a discontinuous rock mass. In particular, they permit the identification of groups of subparallel discontinuities, or 'sets', that may have an important influence upon the behaviour of the rock mass. The mean or some other

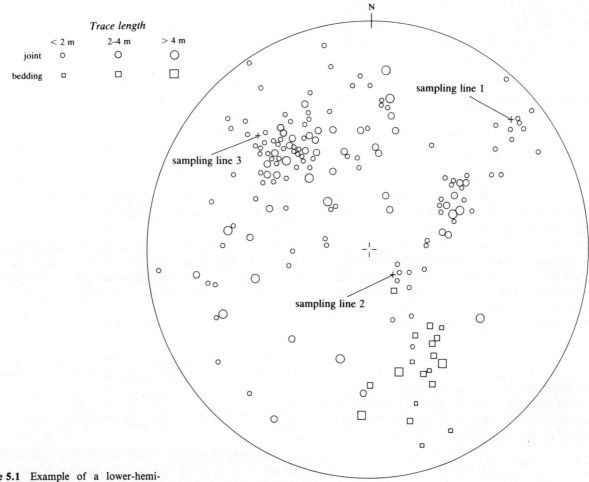

Figure 5.1 Example of a lower-hemisphere plot of discontinuity normals.

representative orientation for each discontinuity set can then be used in subsequent stability analyses. It is worth noting that if lines of maximum dip of discontinuity planes are plotted in addition to their normals, the mean line of maximum dip will not, in general, be equivalent to the mean normal. For most purposes it is preferable to plot only the discontinuity normals.

Before attempting to interpret hemispherical projection plots of discontinuity orientation data, it is important to recognise that any linear sampling regime will bias the sample obtained. The most important of these biases are as follows:

(a) The sampling line will tend to intersect preferentially the larger, or more persistent, discontinuities.
(b) The sampling line will tend to intersect preferentially those discontinuities whose normals make a small angle to the sampling line.

It could be argued that the first bias, listed above, provides a valid emphasis of the larger and therefore structurally more important discontinuities. The nature of this bias has been explained by Priest and Hudson (1981), who also suggest ways in which the bias can be quantified and allowed for if necessary. The second bias, which has been discussed by Terzaghi (1965) and also by Hudson and Priest (1983), has an important influence on the orientation data obtained from a linear survey.

5.2 The sampling bias imposed by a linear survey

Consider a single set of parallel planar discontinuities of dip direction/dip amount α_d/β_d. It is assumed that the frequency of discontinuities from this set, intersected by a sampling line that is normal to the set, is λ per unit length. A sampling line of some general trend/plunge α_s/β_s will encounter a discontinuity frequency λ_s that is less than or equal to λ. Figure 5.2 shows a diagrammatic representation of the discontinuity set, constructed in the plane that contains the normal to the set and the sampling line of general orientation. The acute angle between the sampling line and the set normal is δ. A line, of length l, parallel to the set normal can, for large values of l, be expected to intersect a total number N of discontinuities given by

$$N = \lambda l$$

A general sampling line, at an angle δ to the set normal, would have to be of length $l/\cos\delta$ in order to intersect the same N discontinuities. Hence, the observed frequency along the sampling line is given by

$$\lambda_s = \frac{N \cos \delta}{l}$$

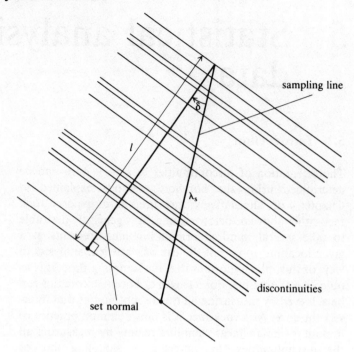

Figure 5.2 Discontinuity set intersected by a sampling line of general orientation.

but

$$\lambda = N/l$$

so

$$\lambda_s = \lambda \cos \delta \tag{5.1}$$

This demonstrates that the number of discontinuities from a given set, intersected by a sampling line that makes an acute angle δ to the set normal, reduces with increasing values of δ and approaches zero when δ approaches 90°. Orientation data from linear sampling lines could, therefore, be severely biased.

It is now possible to consider the general case where there are m sets, each containing parallel, planar discontinuities. The trend and plunge of the line of maximum dip of the ith set are α_{di}/β_{di}, the frequency along the normal to this ith set is λ_i and the acute angle between the normal to the ith set and the sampling line is δ_i, where $i = 1, 2, 3, \ldots, m$. Using Equation 5.1, the frequency λ_{si} of the ith set, measured along the sampling line, is given by

$$\lambda_{si} = \lambda_i \cos \delta_i \tag{5.2}$$

The total fequency, λ_s along the sampling line is given by the sum of the frequency components λ_{si} as follows

$$\lambda_s = \sum_{i=1}^{m} \lambda_{si}$$

The total sample size, N_s, obtained from a sampling line of length l_s, is given by $\lambda_s l_s$. The number N_{si} of discontinuities from the ith set in this sample is given by $\lambda_{si} l_s$ and, therefore, from Equation 5.2 depends partly upon the value of λ_i and partly upon the angle δ_i. Although it is appropriate that the sample size for this ith set should reflect the normal frequency for the set, it is unreasonable that it should also depend upon the, quite arbitrary, angle δ_i. Terzaghi (1965) suggested that this dependence could lead to errors in interpreting the results of discontinuity surveys. In the theoretical case where all the discontinuities within a given set are parallel, this dependence can be removed by dividing N_{si} by $\cos \delta_i$ to give a weighted sample size N_i as follows:

$$N_i = N_{si}/\cos \delta_i = \lambda_i l_s \qquad (5.3)$$

In practice, discontinuities are never orientated in perfectly parallel sets, so it becomes necessary to treat each discontinuity separately. In order to apply the above analysis, it is convenient, for the time being, to consider each separate discontinuity as the member of a different 'set'. The number of 'sets' will, therefore, be the same as the number of discontinuities sampled and the sample size, N_{si}, for each 'set' will be equal to unity. Using Equation 5.3, the weighted sample size for the ith discontinuity 'set' is given by $1/\cos \delta_i$. When applied to a single discontinuity, this weighted sample size will be referred to as the 'weighting factor' w, which, dispensing with the subscript i, is defined as follows

$$w = 1/\cos \delta$$

where δ is the acute angle between the normal to a given discontinuity and the sampling line. The factor w can be calculated analytically as follows, by applying Equation 3.1,

$$w = \frac{1}{|\cos (\alpha_n - \alpha_s) \cos \beta_n \cos \beta_s + \sin \beta_n \sin \beta_s|} \qquad (5.4)$$

where α_s and β_s are the trend and plunge of the sampling line and α_n and β_n are the trend and plunge of the normal to the discontinuity plane, which can be found from the trend and plunge of the line of maximum dip of the plane, as explained in Chapter 1. The 'absolute value' sign is to prevent the generation of negative values for w. Alternatively, the angle δ can be measured directly from the hemispherical projection in the usual way. It may, in fact, be convenient to construct various loci at suitable angular increments from the sampling line, using the construction methods explained in Section 4.2, and to apply a constant weighting factor to all of the data points in a given increment. Whichever of the above methods is used for calculating w, it is necessary to annotate each discontinuity normal, to indicate its weighting factor, on the lower-hemisphere projection. Interpretation of the resulting

diagram must pay due regard to the resulting weighting factors. There are, however, two complications, discussed below, that are associated with this approach.

If the sampling line by chance intersects a single discontinuity whose normal makes an angle of almost 90° with the line, then the weighting factor would be very high. This high weighting could produce a quite spurious concentration of discontinuity normals on the projection and itself lead to an erroneous interpretation of the discontinuity fabric. Additional sampling lines, at right angles to the first, would be needed to check whether there was in fact a real concentration of discontinuity normals at this orientation. A further, and more serious complication arising from this use of weighting factors is that each data point on the hemispherical projection will now be associated with a weighting factor ranging, in theory, from 1 to more than 50 when $\delta = 89°$. Therefore, although the data will have been corrected to remove the sampling bias, the visual impact of the resulting matrix of numbers will be poor. The remainder of this chapter will be devoted to explaining the following three ways of tackling this problem:

(a) Minimise the bias during the sampling process.
(b) Process the data further, by contouring.
(c) Process the data analytically, on a statistical basis.

The easiest way to minimise the bias while sampling is to set up at least three mutually orthogonal sampling lines, of approximately the same length, at a given location. Any discontinuities that tend to be ignored by one sampling line, as a result of having a large angle δ, will tend to be sampled preferentially by one or both of the other sampling lines. This tendency for the sampling bias to cancel out means that the aggregated data for the sampling lines will provide a reasonable representation of the discontinuity fabric. In theory, however, the sampling bias is not completely removed. Consider, for example, three mutually orthogonal scanlines a, b and c, each of length 10 m, that intersect a persistent set of parallel, planar discontinuities whose frequency along the set normal is 8.4 m^{-1}. Let δ_a, δ_b and δ_c be respectively the acute angles between this set normal and the sampling lines a, b and c. If $\delta_a = 0$ and $\delta_b = \delta_c = 90°$, then, by using Equation 5.2, approximately 84 discontinuities from this set would be present in the aggregated sample from the three scanlines. At the other extreme, if $\delta_a = \delta_b = \delta_c = \arccos (1/\sqrt{3}) = 54.74°$, then, again using Equation 5.2, approximately 145 discontinuities from this set would be present in the aggregated sample. This residual bias, although still significant, is considerably less than that associated with a single scanline. The use of orthogonal scanlines has a further attraction, in that there is no need to apply any weighting factors; the orientation data can simply be plotted as shown in Figure 5.1 and then interpreted without further processing. From a practical geological point of view, any significant preferred orientation(s) in the discontinuity fabric should be apparent as clusters of normals in such a diagram. Indeed, the use of further processing and contouring often has the detrimental effect of obscuring the original data and generating spurious concentrations. In the author's opinion, contouring can only be justified where the application of weighting factors has generated a matrix of numbers on the hemispherical projection, which inevitably has poor visual impact.

5.3 Contouring methods

The contouring of orientation data is a three-stage process:

(1) Each discontinuity normal is plotted, together with its associated weighting factor, on a lower-hemisphere projection.
(2) A sampling window is placed over the data, to generate a matrix of moving average values, representing the variation in the concentration of discontinuity normals over the projection.
(3) The moving average values are contoured at some appropriate interval.

When there is a large number of data points, this process can become very laborious and time-consuming, and is best carried out by a computer with some form of plotting capability. Contouring can, however, be carried out manually if desired. The following method is probably the simplest of those available.

The first stage involves plotting the discontinuity normals, and the associated weighting factors for the appropriate sampling line, on a lower-hemisphere projection. Although, in theory, an equal-area projection should be used since it minimises the areal distortion effects, in practice there is little to choose between the results obtained from this and an equal-angle projection (Hoek & Brown 1980). There is clearly no point in using the different sizes and shapes of symbols, as shown in Figure 5.1, to represent different sizes and types of discontinuities since the original data will be replaced by a contoured diagram. For a given sampling line, the weighted sample size is simply the sum of all the separate weighting factors w, calculated using Equation 5.4 for each of the discontinuities intersected by the sampling line. If data from several sampling lines are plotted on the same diagram, the total weighted sample size is the sum of the separate values of w for each sampling line.

A moving average is obtained by finding the total weighted subsample that appears within a small window placed over the data points on the projection. It is usually convenient to design the window so that its area is 1% of the area of projection. If a circular window is used it must, therefore, have a radius a that is one-tenth of that for the

projection. The use of a window of constant size imposes a slight distortion. For example, if an equal-angle projection has been used, a 1% circular window located at the centre of the projection subtends a solid angle of approximately 23°; near the perimeter it subtends a solid angle of approximately 12°. The correponding angles for an equal-area projection are approximately 16° and 22° respectively. This shows that the distortion is reduced, but not completely eradicated, when a circular window is used on an equal-area projection. Ideally, to remove this distortion, it would be necessary to change the area (or, on the equal-area projection, the shape) of the window as a function of its distance from the centre of the projection. In practice, this refinement is rarely justified since a computer-based contouring package can be employed when a precise result is required.

The following manual method assumes that a circular counting window will be used; this counting circle can be either drawn on tracing paper or cut into a perspex sheet. Before proceeding with the counting process, it is necessary to construct a square grid, with a line spacing a, to provide reference points for the counting circle. This grid is drawn on tracing paper and fixed on top of the projection containing the data points that are to be contoured. Finally, a sheet of plain tracing paper, with the circle of projection and north point marked on, is fixed over the grid, as shown in Figure 5.3a. The counting circle is positioned with its centre at a grid intersection point and the total weighted subsample within the circle is calculated. If weighting factors have been applied to the data points, this will involve adding up all the separate weighting values for the points falling inside the counting circle. This total subsample is then expressed as a percentage of the total weighted sample size and recorded at the grid point on the overlay. Figure 5.3b shows the overlapping positions for the counting circle as its centre is moved to each grid point in turn. If the total weighted sample size in Figure 5.3a is, say, 275.63, then the percentages of weighted values per 1% area of the projection are as shown in Figure 5.3b. These percentage values should be marked close to the grid point, at the centre of the appropriate counting circle. It is, of course, only necessary to use the counting circle in areas where it will contain at least one data point. When the counting circle is close to the edge of the net, any part of the circle that extends beyond the perimeter must re-enter at a diametrically opposite point. This necessity to operate the counting circle in two separate parts can be satisfied by cutting two counting circles into a perspex sheet, with their centres one net-diameter apart as shown in Figure 5.3a. It is usually helpful to record the resulting percentage value in both of the counting circles when operating at the perimeter of the net in this way.

When the counting process is complete, the overlay, containing the matrix of percentage values, can be removed and contoured. A contour interval of 1% is usually

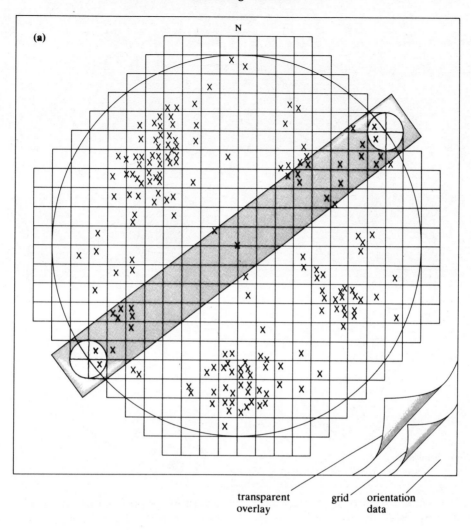

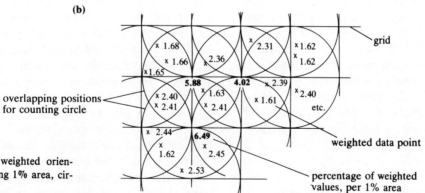

Figure 5.3 Contouring weighted orientation data using a moving 1% area, circular window.

satisfactory for most purposes, although an interval of 2% may be required where there is a significant clustering of the normals. The contouring process is largely a matter of personal judgement and skill. It is important to remember, however, that if a given contour crosses the perimeter of the projection, it must re-enter the projection at a diametrically opposite point. Finally, the inter-contour zones can be shaded to emphasise the different concentra-

tions, as shown in Figure 5.4. It was noted earlier that the correction of sampling bias can produce anomalously high weighting factors when the angle δ approaches $90°$. This, in turn, can lead to high concentrations on the resulting contour diagram. Such concentrations should be treated with caution, unless they can be verified using additional sampling lines.

For many applications in rock mechanics, it is necessary

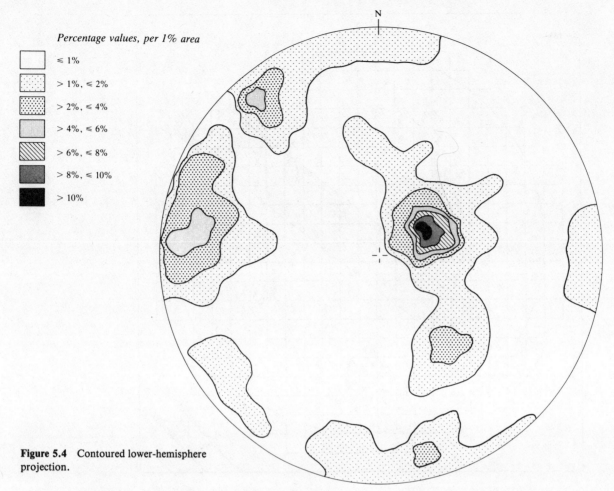

Percentage values, per 1% area

□ ≤ 1%

▨ > 1%, ≤ 2%

▨ > 2%, ≤ 4%

▨ > 4%, ≤ 6%

▨ > 6%, ≤ 8%

▨ > 8%, ≤ 10%

■ > 10%

Figure 5.4 Contoured lower-hemisphere projection.

to identify clusters of discontinuity normals that represent groups, or 'sets', of subparallel discontinuities. These applications usually require single orientation values that are representative of the discontinuities in each set. For most practical purposes this representative orientation can be assessed by eye as the 'centre of gravity' of a cluster of normals or the 'high point' of an area on a contoured diagram. This approach, however, provides no measure of the degree to which the normals are clustered. Moreover, it may be difficult to assess the representative orientation of a cluster that is asymmetrical or widely distributed over the projection. In such cases, a more rigorous statistical approach may be required.

5.4 Analysis of the clustering of discontinuity normals

There are several different statistical methods that can be applied to analysing discontinuity orientations in three dimensions. The most important of these have been explained by Krumbein and Graybill (1965), Koch and Link (1971) and Till (1974). Some of these methods use fairly sophisticated statistical models to discriminate between overlapping clusters of discontinuity normals, to

determine representative orientations and to obtain a measure of the degree of clustering within each set. These statistical approaches are beyond the scope of this book and, being adequately described elsewhere, will not be considered further. There is, however, one approach, described below, that is inherently very simple and lends itself well to problems in rock mechanics.

A typical discontinuity sample may contain many hundreds of orientation values obtained from several sampling lines of different orientations. The first step in the analysis is to plot each discontinuity normal as a single point on a lower-hemisphere projection. In view of the fact that the subsequent analysis is best carried out by a computer, it may be convenient to plot these orientation data using computer graphics rather than by hand. The basic theory, to enable computer plotting, is explained below.

The raw data, giving the orientation of a given discontinuity, will usually be in terms of the trend α_d and the plunge β_d of its line of maximum dip. The trend α_n and plunge β_n of the normal to this discontinuity are given by

$$\alpha_n = \alpha_d \pm 180° \qquad 0° \leq \alpha_n \leq 360° \qquad (5.5)$$

$$\beta_n = 90° - \beta_d \qquad (5.6)$$

44

(a)

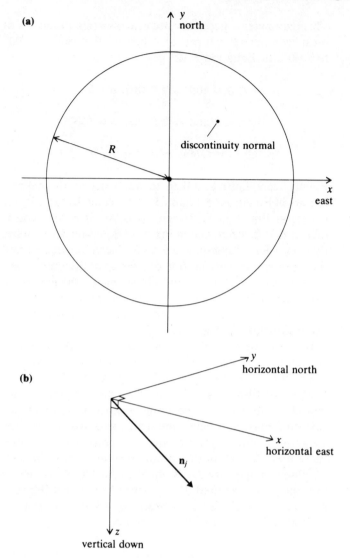

(b)

Figure 5.5 Cartesian co-ordinate systems.

Table 5.1 The x, y Cartesian co-ordinates of a point on a lower-hemisphere projection of radius R.

	x	y
equal-angle projection	$R \sin \alpha_n \tan\left(45 - \dfrac{\beta_n}{2}\right)$	$R \cos \alpha_n \tan\left(45 - \dfrac{\beta_n}{2}\right)$
equal-area projection	$R\sqrt{2} \sin \alpha_n \cos\left(45 + \dfrac{\beta_n}{2}\right)$	$R\sqrt{2} \cos \alpha_n \cos\left(45 + \dfrac{\beta_n}{2}\right)$

values of $210° < \alpha_n \leqslant 265°$ while set 2 may generally occur between $240° < \alpha_n \leqslant 315°$. In some cases it may also be necessary to specify the range of plunge values for a given set. Alternatively the boundary orientations for a given set can be defined by a cone angle measured from an axis placed near to the central orientation of a given cluster of normals. The analysis described below is carried out on only those discontinuities that belong to a given set as defined by one of the above methods. If there is some overlap between a pair of adjacent sets, it may be desirable to analyse them first separately and then aggregated.

Equation 5.4 shows how the weighting factor w can be calculated for a discontinuity that is intersected by a sampling line of trend/plunge α_s/β_s. Consider a group of N discontinuities that are assumed to belong to the same set. Let the normal to the jth of these discontinuities have a trend α_{nj} and plunge β_{nj}, and be associated with a weighting factor w_j, calculated using Equation 5.4. The total weighted sample size, N_w, for the set is given by

$$N_w = \sum_{j=1}^{N} w_j \qquad (5.7)$$

Each of the weighting factors w_j will be greater than or equal to 1.0; consequently N_w will usually be greater than N, with typical values for the ratio N_w/N lying between 2 and 5. This increase in the effective sample size was of little consequence in the previous section because the contoured diagrams were presented in terms of percentage values. The sample size is of critical importance, however, when estimating the precision of the data. In view of this it is necessary to normalise each of the weighting factors w_j so that the total normalised weighted sample size is equal to N. The normalised weighting factors w_j' are given by

$$w_j' = w_j N/N_w \qquad (5.8)$$

so that

$$\sum_{j=1}^{N} w_j' = N$$

The ratio N/N_w is constant and does not, therefore, change the relative weighting values. Two passes through

It is necessary to ensure that α_n lies between $0°$ and $360°$ only if the data are to be plotted by hand.

Figure 5.5a shows a circular area of projection of radius R, related to an x, y Cartesian co-ordinate system in which positive x is horizontal to the east (trend $90°$) and positive y is horizontal to the north (trend $0°$). The x, y Cartesian co-ordinates of the projection of the discontinuity normal, of trend/plunge α_n/β_n, are given in Table 5.1 for equal-angle and equal-area projections.

The expressions in Table 5.1 can be used as a basis for a simple computer program to plot a lower-hemisphere projection of the complete sample of discontinuity normals. Whether constructed by computer or by hand, the resulting diagram is used to identify the approximate boundary orientations of the various discontinuity sets. If the orientation data are widely scattered, the zones covered by adjacent sets may overlap to some degree. For example, set 1 may appear to occur between the approximate trend the orientation data for the set are required: the first to evaluate N_w using Equations 5.4 and 5.7, the second to evaluate the normalised weighting factors w_j' using Equation 5.8.

The jth discontinuity can be represented by a vector, of magnitude w_j', orientated parallel to the discontinuity normal. Figure 5.5b shows a left-handed Cartesian coordinate system in which positive x is horizontal to the east (trend $90°$), positive y is horizontal to the north (trend $0°$) and positive z is vertically down (plunge $90°$). This, perhaps unusual, use of a left-handed system maintains compatibility with the two-dimensional system in Figure 5.5a, while ensuring that the lower-hemisphere projection exists on the positive z side of the xy plane. The x, y and z Cartesian components of the terminal point of the vector $\mathbf{n}_j$ of magnitude w_j', which has its initial point at the origin and is aligned parallel to the jth discontinuity normal are given by n_{jx}, n_{jy} and n_{jz} as follows

$$n_{jx} = w_j' \sin \alpha_{nj} \cos \beta_{nj}$$

$$n_{jy} = w_j' \cos \alpha_{nj} \cos \beta_{nj} \qquad (5.9)$$

$$n_{jz} = w_j' \sin \beta_{nj}$$

It is assumed that the representative orientation or mean normal for this set is given by the orientation of the resultant of the vectors $\mathbf{n}_j$ where $j = 1$ to N. This approach has the advantage of automatically attaching greater importance to those orientations that carry a higher weighting factor. The x, y and z Cartesian components of this resultant, or mean, vector $\mathbf{r}_n$ are given by r_x, r_y and r_z as follows

$$r_x = \sum_{j=1}^{N} n_{jx}$$

$$r_y = \sum_{j=1}^{N} n_{jy} \qquad (5.10)$$

$$r_z = \sum_{j=1}^{N} n_{jz}$$

The magnitude of $\mathbf{r}_n$ is given by R_w as follows

$$R_w = \sqrt{(r_x^2 + r_y^2 + r_z^2)} \qquad (5.11)$$

The trend α_{rn} and plunge β_{rn} of $\mathbf{r}_n$ are as follows

$$\alpha_{rn} = \arctan (r_x/r_y) + q \qquad (5.12)$$

$$\beta_{rn} = \arctan [r_z/\sqrt{(r_x^2 + r_y^2)}] \qquad (5.13)$$

The parameter q is an angle, in degrees, that ensures that α_{rn} lies in the correct quadrant and in the range 0 to $360°$.

This parameter is necessary because the arctan function of most computers returns a value in the range $-90°$ to $+90°$. In Equation 5.12

$$\text{if } r_x \geqslant 0 \text{ and } r_y \geqslant 0 \text{ then } q = 0$$

$$\text{if } r_x < 0 \text{ and } r_y \geqslant 0 \text{ then } q = 360°$$

$$\text{for all other signs of } r_x \text{ and } r_y, \ q = 180°$$

Finally, care must be taken to test whether the denominators in Equations 5.12 and 5.13 are equal to zero. If this occurs in Equation 5.12 then α_{rn} is $90°$ if $r_x > 0$, and is $270°$ if $r_x < 0$; a zero denominator in Equation 5.13 implies that $\beta_{rn} = 90°$. Equations 5.9 to 5.13 can be used to find the representative orientation of a group of discontinuities, in terms of the trend α_{rn} and plunge β_{rn} of the normal to the representative plane. The orientation of the line of maximum dip of this plane can be found from α_{rn} and β_{rn} using Equations 5.5 and 5.6.

It can be useful to obtain some measure of the degree of clustering in a given set. This problem was considered indirectly by Fisher (1953) in a generalised statistical analysis of dispersion on a sphere. His analysis did not consider the use of weighting factors to correct for sampling bias, and hence implicitly assumed that all the weighting values w_j were equal to unity. In this case, therefore, each vector $\mathbf{n}_j$ is of unit magnitude and the total weighted sample size N_w is equal to N. Normalisation is not, therefore, required. Fisher defined a factor K (Fisher's constant), which is a measure of clustering that is estimated from N and R_w, as follows

$$K = \frac{N-1}{N - R_w} \qquad (5.14)$$

If all the discontinuities in the set are nearly parallel, then R_w approaches N and hence K approaches infinity. If the discontinuities are randomly orientated then R_w, and hence K, becomes small. In theory, the minimum value of K is close to unity; in practice K is rarely less than about 5.

In order to correct for sampling bias it is necessary to apply weighting factors that are not equal to unity. In the remainder of this chapter it is assumed that Fisher's methods are applicable to the analysis of weighted data if these data have been normalised, using Equation 5.8, to ensure that the total normalised weighted sample size is equal to N. The errors introduced by this approximating assumption are considerably less than those that would be introduced by simply ignoring the sampling bias.

Fisher made the fundamental assumption that the population of vectors (from which $\mathbf{n}_j$ are samples) is randomly dispersed about some 'true' orientation. In the present context, this is equivalent to the idea of discontinuity normals being dispersed within a set. Fisher also assumed that the probability $P(\theta)$ that a vector selected at random (i.e. without bias) from the population makes a solid angle of between θ and $\theta + d\theta$ with the true orientation is given by

$$P(\theta) = \nu\,e^{K\cos\theta}\,d\theta \qquad (5.15)$$

where ν is a value that incorporates the following requirements:

(a) The area of an annulus of width $d\theta$ at an angle θ from the true orientation is proportional to $\sin\theta$. The value of $P(\theta)$ must, therefore, also be proportional to $\sin\theta$.
(b) The sum of all possible values of $P(\theta)$ must be unity.

These requirements give the following result

$$\nu = \frac{K\sin\theta}{e^{K} - e^{-K}} \qquad (5.16)$$

When K is large, the distribution in Equations 5.15 and 5.16 tends to conform to a two-dimensional isotropic Gaussian distribution in which the variance is $1/K$. When the sample size N is large (greater than about 30), it becomes possible to write down fairly simple approximations for the following probabilities:

(a) $P_1(<\theta)$, the probability that a vector selected at random from the population makes a solid angle of less than θ with the true orientation; and
(b) $P_2(<\theta)$, the probability that the resultant vector $\mathbf{r}_n$ makes a solid angle of less than θ with the true orientation,

where

$$P_1\,(<\theta) \simeq 1 - e^{-K(1-\cos\theta)} \qquad (5.17)$$

which when inverted gives

$$\cos\theta \simeq 1 + \frac{\log_e\,[1 - P_1\,(<\theta)]}{K} \qquad (5.18)$$

and

$$P_2(<\theta) \simeq 1 - e^{-KR_w(1-\cos\theta)} \qquad (5.19)$$

for which the inverse is

$$\cos\theta \simeq 1 + \frac{\log_e\,[1 - P_2(<\theta)]}{KR_w} \qquad (5.20)$$

Equations 5.17 and 5.18 can be used to test how well the distribution model fits a given group of orientation values. To do this it is first necessary to assume that the resultant

vector $\mathbf{r}_n$ represents the best estimate of the unknown true orientation. Conical loci at suitable intervals of cone angle θ can then be constructed about $\mathbf{r}_n$. The model predicts that a proportion $P_1\,(<\theta)$ of an unbiased sample should occur inside the locus associated with a cone angle θ. The actual and theoretical values can be plotted on graph paper to provide a visual assessment of the suitability of the model. More sophisticated goodness-of-fit test, such as the chi-square test, can be applied if necessary. If it is found that the distribution model accords reasonably well with the observed data, then Equations 5.18 and 5.20 can be used to define ranges of likely discontinuity orientation on the projection. If the prime concern is the likely range of orientations for individual discontinuities, then Equation 5.18, associated with $P_1(<\theta)$, would be used. If, on the other hand, it is more important to define the likely range for the mean orientation of the set, then Equation 5.20, associated with $P_2(<\theta)$, would be used. For example, using Equation 5.18, there is 0.8 probability that a discontinuity normal selected at random from the set will lie within a locus, centred on $\mathbf{r}_n$, that has a cone angle given by arccos $[1 + (\log_e (1-0.8)/K)]$. Loci defined in this way would provide, for example, a good basis for carrying out a sensitivity analysis on the stability of individual rigid rock blocks. Alternatively, using Equation 5.20, there is for example 0.95 probability that the true mean orientation for the set lies inside a locus, centred on $\mathbf{r}_n$, that has a cone angle given by arccos $[1 + (\log_e (1-0.95)/KR_w)]$. The zone defined by Equation 5.20 is usually termed the 'zone of confidence'. In this case there is 95% confidence that the true mean orientation lies inside the specified locus. Loci defined in this way provide a good basis for evaluating the structure of a given rock mass and, in particular, for comparing data obtained from different locations.

Example 5.1 (Tables 5.2 & 5.3, Figs 5.6 & 5.7) The following hypothetical example serves to illustrate the cluster analysis presented above. Table 5.2 is a list of the orientations of 162 discontinuities obtained from sample lines 1 and 2, of trend/plunge 349/05 and 192/10 respectively. Figure 5.6 is a simple, computer-generated equal-angle plot of the normals to these discontinuities, together with the orientations of the two sample lines. Visual inspection of this plot led to the division of the data into three basic sets, according to the ranges of normals listed in Table 5.3. A fourth set was obtained by aggregating sets 2 and 3. Each of these sets was analysed to determine the orientation of the mean normal and Fisher's constant, using the equations presented earlier. This analysis was first carried out without weighting for sample line orientation and was then repeated for each set, this time applying weighting and normalisation factors. This latter analysis is indicated by the letter 'w' in the first column of Table 5.3. The results in this table show that the orientation of the

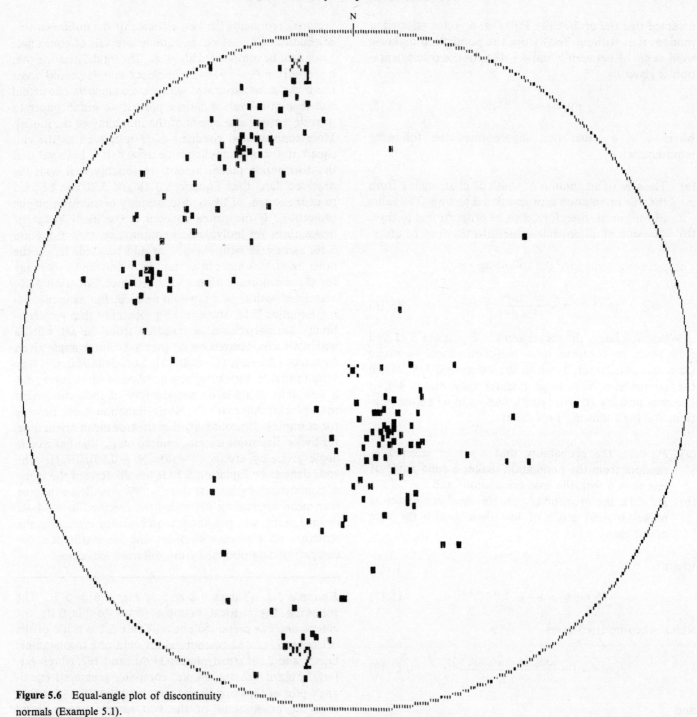

Figure 5.6 Equal-angle plot of discontinuity normals (Example 5.1).

mean normal can change when the data are weighted. This effect is only significant, however, for the sets that are relatively widely dispersed and, therefore, have relatively small values for Fisher's constant.

Figures 5.7a and 5.7b are examples of graphs of the proportion $P(< \theta)$ of discontinuity normals that make a solid angle of less than θ with the resultant vector or mean normal for a given set. Figure 5.7a shows the graph of $P(< \theta)$ against θ for unweighted data from set 1; Figure 5.7b shows the graph for weighted data from sets 2 and 3 aggregated. Each figure also contains the theoretical graph of $P(< \theta)$, given by $P_1(< \theta)$ in Equation 5.17. These graphs, which are derived from hypothetical data, are presented for illustrative purposes only and should not be taken to confirm or disprove the validity of Fisher's model. Because this model may be applicable for some rock masses and not for others, it is advisable to construct graphs like those in Figure 5.7 to assess the validity of the model for a given group of values.

Table 5.2 Hypothetical discontinuity orientation data (Example 5.1).

(a) Sample line 1, 349/05		(b) Sample line 2, 192/10	
Dip direction/dip amount		Dip direction/dip amount	
003/68	156/69	000/38	157/71
004/49	158/76	002/68	157/73
008/77	158/80	003/32	160/63
009/85	158/84	003/47	160/71
011/77	159/75	005/77	160/72
017/24	163/74	008/72	160/79
018/24	166/85	009/76	164/77
018/87	168/79	011/52	166/80
019/74	168/82	012/27	168/71
050/58	171/84	014/72	170/77
107/69	218/26	014/80	173/73
108/81	263/10	015/78	190/67
110/72	267/10	017/50	232/66
113/67	267/34	029/76	263/20
113/68	297/61	036/67	278/68
114/70	300/56	044/18	286/24
115/72	306/46	052/56	286/53
116/63	307/14	093/57	291/25
116/66	315/33	094/77	302/26
116/68	320/17	100/65	304/17
119/68	320/22	109/68	313/21
123/69	321/31	111/71	313/27
124/77	323/27	113/62	318/33
126/48	327/24	113/74	324/24
131/68	329/21	114/67	327/17
132/75	329/31	115/69	328/62
133/69	331/25	118/70	329/23
139/64	332/16	120/54	329/27
139/72	332/44	125/77	330/38
141/52	332/60	130/64	333/28
141/77	335/38	132/81	335/23
147/71	335/47	133/67	336/44
149/75	336/25	147/73	337/35
150/70	347/47	151/72	337/46
150/81	348/23	152/66	339/31
152/57	351/30	152/70	340/26
152/72	353/11	153/72	342/22
152/73	354/61	153/74	345/30
154/71	355/42	154/78	351/38
154/75	356/36	154/89	352/16
		156/74	352/26

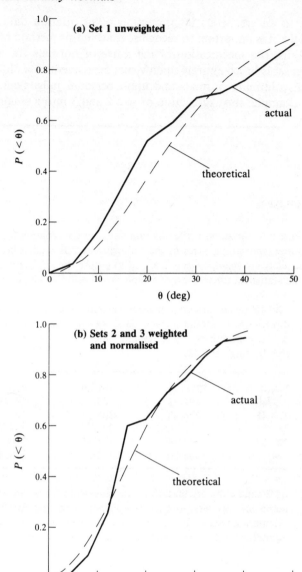

Figure 5.7 Graphs of the proportion, $P(<\theta)$, of discontinuity normals that make a solid angle of less than θ with the mean normal (Example 5.1).

Table 5.3 Statistical analysis of discontinuity normals plotted in Figure 5.6 (Example 5.1)

	Range of normals				Mean normal	
Set	Trend (deg)	Plunge (deg)	Number of values	Fisher's constant	Trend (deg)	Plunge (deg)
1	030–260	0–90	86	7.42	165.2	55.0
1w				7.47	113.8	57.0
2	260–325	0–90	36	36.18	299.3	22.2
2w				49.68	293.6	22.7
3	315–030	0–90	44	49.47	337.0	16.6
3w				50.50	336.6	17.0
2 and 3	260–030	0–90	76	13.56	320.5	19.8
2w and 3w				14.43	304.9	22.2

If it can be shown that Fisher's model is valid, then Equation 5.20 can be used to construct confidence zones on the projection. For example, the 90% and 95% confidence zones centred on the mean normal for unweighted values from set 1 in the above example have cone angles of $5.23°$ and $5.96°$ respectively. The corresponding angles for weighted values from this set are $5.21°$ and $5.94°$. If these were real data, the conclusion would be that there is 95% certainty that the true mean orientation for this set lies within approximately $6°$ of the computed mean for both the unweighted and weighted analyses. The mean normals for the unweighted and weighted data for this set are, however, $28.1°$ apart. This shows how sample bias can lead to an erroneous interpretation of orientation data. Finally, it is important to recognise that, in this method of analysis, the specification of the range of normals for a given set is based entirely upon visual assessment of a plot of discontinuity normals and upon personal judgement. For example, the aggregation of sets 2 and 3 into a single set leads to a very different interpretation of the above data. In general, it is better to evaluate several different specifications for the ranges of normals and to aggregate the basic sets in various different ways before drawing conclusions about the rock structure.

Exercises

In order to minimise the amount of routine computation required, the sample sizes in the following exercises have been kept relatively small. In practice, and to ensure the applicability of the statistical theory, larger sample sizes would be required.

5.1 The following orientation measurements, recorded as dip direction/dip amount of each plane, were obtained for a set of discontinuities by sampling along a scanline of trend/plunge 165/11.

269/61	296/68	301/49	320/55
273/40	297/58	305/52	322/36
277/41	298/47	306/55	327/62
283/53	298/50	307/47	329/70
292/38	299/54	311/57	330/63
294/51	300/26	312/70	338/59

(i) Estimate the orientation of the representative or 'mean' plane for this set. (ii) Calculate Fisher's constant for the orientation measurements. (iii) Estimate the probability that a randomly selected normal from the set will make an angle of (a) less than $10°$ and (b) more than $25°$ with the mean normal for the set.

Obtain answers first without weighting for sample line orientation and then by applying appropriate weighting and normalisation factors.

5.2 Orientation measurements were taken at random locations on the surface of a large, undulating discontinuity surface in order to estimate its mean orientation. The following values, recorded as dip direction/dip amount were obtained.

074/13	123/30	136/27	150/35
095/35	125/17	137/25	150/44
113/23	131/26	138/39	154/22
117/42	132/24	139/28	161/34
119/33	135/32	146/33	174/29

(i) Estimate the mean orientation of the discontinuity surface. (ii) Calculate Fisher's constant for the orientation measurements. (iii) Calculate the angular radii for the zones of (a) 95% confidence and (b) 99% confidence on the mean normal.

Answers to these exercises are given on page 123.

6 Analysis of forces

6.1 Introduction

It is often necessary, in rock mechanics studies, to consider the effects of forces acting on a given body. A force is a vector quantity in that it has both orientation and magnitude. For example, the orientation of a force of magnitude F could be specified in terms of the trend α and plunge β of the line along which the force acts.

Hemispherical projection methods offer an important tool for the graphical representation and analysis of the *orientation* properties of vectors. It is, however, very difficult to represent and analyse vector *magnitudes* on a hemispherical projection. Consequently, for the complete analysis of vector quantities such as force, hemispherical projection methods must be supplemented by further calculations or graphical constructions. In many cases the simplest approach is to represent each vector by its cartesian components in three dimensions, and to carry out the vector analysis using the standard techniques of vector algebra[1]. The hemispherical projection is then only used to present the input and output data in graphical form. For example, it is often the case in rock mechanics studies that the body under analysis is a rigid block whose geometry is defined by discontinuity planes of some specified orientations. In such cases it is usually convenient to carry out any preliminary geometrical analysis using hemispherical projection methods, but to transfer to vector algebra methods for the analysis of the associated forces. All of the forces involved can be plotted on the hemispherical projection for further geometrical analysis if required. This approach, which is adopted in this book, has the advantage of facilitating visualisation of the physical realities of a problem by emphasising the relation between the rock mass geometry and the associated forces. Some of the vector algebra methods described in this chapter require fairly lengthy calculations that are best carried out by computer. In some cases, however, it is possible to shorten and simplify these calculations by further utilising hemispherical projection methods. Wherever possible in this chapter, therefore, the explanations of vector algebra methods will be followed by descriptions of equivalent graphical methods, based on hemispherical projection techniques, that minimise the routine computation and incur only a small reduction in precision.

When several forces act on a body, it is assumed for simplicity throughout this book that the forces act through a common point, which in most cases will be the centre of mass of the body. This simplification removes the need to consider rotation of the body and the associated equations of moment equilibrium.

6.2 Representation of a force vector

A force, represented by the vector quantity **u**, can be defined in terms of the three components u_x, u_y and u_z of its terminal point relative to a set of Cartesian co-ordinate axes x, y and z, which are located so that the initial point of the vector lies at their origin. The left-handed set of axes illustrated in Figure 6.1 is the one used in Chapter 5, in

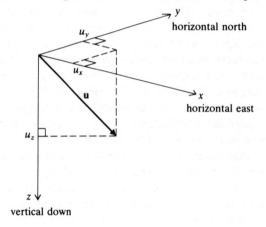

Figure 6.1 Vector in three dimensions.

which positive x is horizontal to the east, positive y is horizontal to the north and positive z is vertically down. This Cartesian co-ordinate system will be used throughout this chapter and also in the various examples and exercises. The magnitude of a vector can be found directly from its three Cartesian components; for example the magnitude of **u** is given by

$$|\mathbf{u}| = \sqrt{(u_x^2 + u_y^2 + u_z^2)} \tag{6.1}$$

which, in this case, gives the magnitude of the force. If $|\mathbf{u}|$ is equal to 1.0, the vector is termed a unit vector and its Cartesian components are usually called direction cosines.

The trend α and plunge β of a line parallel to **u** are given by

$$\alpha = \arctan(u_x/u_y) + q \tag{6.2}$$

[1] The text by Spiegel (1974) is recommended to those readers who wish to pursue this subject further.

$$\beta = \arctan \left[u_z / \sqrt{(u_x^2 + u_y^2)} \right] \qquad (6.3)$$

where q is an angle, discussed in connection with Equations 5.12 and 5.13, that ensures that α lies in the correct quadrant and in the range 0 to 360°:

if $u_x \geqslant 0$ and $u_y \geqslant 0$ then $q = 0$

if $u_x < 0$ and $u_y \geqslant 0$ then $q = 360°$

for all other signs of u_x and u_y, $q = 180°$

As before, care must be taken when the denominators in Equations 6.2 and 6.3 are zero.

If the Cartesian components of a given force vector are known, then Equations 6.2 and 6.3 can be used to calculate its trend and plunge, and thereby allow the vector to be plotted as a point on a lower-hemisphere projection. There are two minor complications in doing this. Firstly, because a projection can only represent *orientation* data in graphical form, it is necessary to annotate the point in order to indicate the magnitude of the force whose orientation it represents. Secondly, if u_z were negative then β would be negative also, and the point would plot on the upper hemisphere and not the lower hemisphere of projection. This problem can be overcome by plotting the reverse direction of those vectors for which the z Cartesian component is negative. The Cartesian components of this reverse vector are obtained simply by multiplying the original x, y and z Cartesian components by -1.0 *before* applying Equations 6.2 and 6.3. This ensures that β is always positive and that all vectors can be plotted and analysed on the lower hemisphere of projection. Taking the reverse vector in this way changes neither the magnitude nor the orientation of the line of action of the original force vector. It is necessary, however, to annotate each point not only to indicate the magnitude of the vector that it represents, but also to indicate whether the original vector has a downward sense (positive z Cartesian component) or an upward sense (negative z Cartesian component). This concept of the sense of a force has the advantage of providing a natural logical link with the principles of action and reaction embodied in Newton's third law of motion.

It is now possible to write down the inverse forms of Equations 6.2 and 6.3. Consider a vector of known magnitude $|\mathbf{u}|$ acting along a line of trend α and plunge β. The Cartesian components of the vector $\mathbf{u}$, relative to the set of axes defined in Figure 6.1, are given by

$$\begin{aligned} u_x &= S \, |\mathbf{u}| \sin \alpha \cos \beta \\ u_y &= S \, |\mathbf{u}| \cos \alpha \cos \beta \\ u_z &= S \, |\mathbf{u}| \sin \beta \end{aligned} \qquad (6.4)$$

The sense of the force is represented by the parameter S, which takes a value $+1.0$ if the force has a downward

sense and -1.0 if it has an upward sense. A horizontal force has a sense of $+1.0$ if it acts in the direction of the specified trend and a sense of -1.0 if it acts in the opposite direction. It is, therefore, possible to convert between the Cartesian component representation used in vector algebra and the polar representation, in terms of trend, plunge, magnitude and sense, required for plotting on a hemispherical projection. The following examples illustrate this. In these, and subsequent examples and exercises, the results will be quoted to more significant figures than would normally be justified; this is to facilitate checking.

Example 6.1 (Fig. 6.2) The x, y and z Cartesian components of the force vectors $\mathbf{u}$ and $\mathbf{v}$, relative to the set of axes defined in Figure 6.1, are respectively

$u_x =$	1.83 kN	$v_x =$	4.25 kN
$u_y =$	-3.29 kN	$v_y =$	-1.78 kN
$u_z =$	2.47 kN	$v_z =$	-6.53 kN

Plot these force vectors on a lower-hemisphere projection.

The z Cartesian component of $\mathbf{u}$ is positive; therefore the force has a downward sense. The signs of u_x and u_y require that the parameter q in Equation 6.2 is equal to 180°; hence for $\mathbf{u}$, using Equations 6.1 to 6.3,

$|\mathbf{u}| = 4.503$ kN with a downward sense
$\alpha = 150.9°$
$\beta = 33.3°$

The z Cartesian component of $\mathbf{v}$ is negative; therefore the force has an upward sense and it is only possible to plot the reverse vector which has x, y and z Cartesian components of -4.25, 1.78 and 6.53 kN respectively. The signs of the x and y Cartesian components of this reverse vector require that the parameter q in Equation 6.2 is equal to 360°; hence for $\mathbf{v}$

$|\mathbf{v}| = 7.992$ kN with an upward sense
$\alpha = 292.7°$
$\beta = 54.8°$

The two force vectors are plotted in Figure 6.2.

Example 6.2 A force of magnitude 6.34 kN acts in an upward sense along a line of trend 215° and plunge 69°. Determine the x, y and z Cartesian components of this force, relative to the set of axes defined in Figure 6.1.

The parameter S in Equations 6.4 is set to -1.0 because the force has an upward sense. These equations give the x, y and z Cartesian components of the force as 1.303, 1.861 and -5.919 kN respectively.

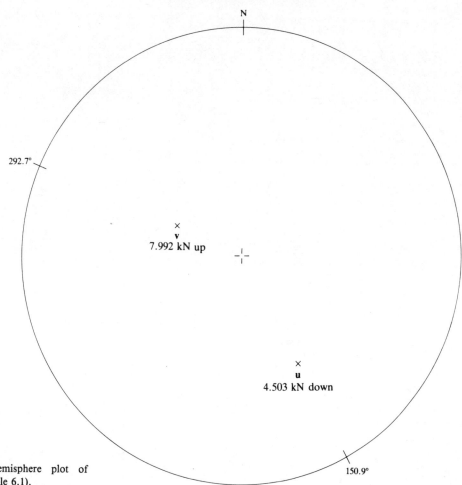

Figure 6.2 Lower-hemisphere plot of force vectors (Example 6.1).

6.3 The resultant of forces

The resultant of two or more forces can be found by the method of vector addition, which is explained briefly below. Consider, for example, three forces, represented by the vector quantities **u**, **v** and **w** with Cartesian components u_x, u_y, u_z, v_x, v_y, v_z, w_x, w_y and w_z respectively, and which are assumed to act at the same point. The combined effects of the three forces can be represented by a single hypothetical resultant vector $\mathbf{r} = \mathbf{u} + \mathbf{v} + \mathbf{w}$ which has Cartesian components r_x, r_y and r_z, given respectively by $u_x + v_x + w_x$, $u_y + v_y + w_y$ and $u_z + v_z + w_z$. The resultant of any number of vectors acting at a point can be found by summing their Cartesian components algebraically in this way. This important property of vectors was used in Chapter 5 for the statistical analysis of discontinuity normals. In the above illustration, a fourth force with Cartesian components $-r_x$, $-r_y$ and $-r_z$ would be required to act at the given point in order to maintain static equilibrium with the forces **u**, **v** and **w**.

Example 6.3 (Fig. 6.3) The following three forces act at a point:

Force	Trend (deg)	Plunge (deg)	Magnitude (kN)	Sense
u	132	61	7.3	up
v	347	27	6.1	down
w	266	48	12.5	up

Find the trend, plunge, magnitude and sense of the resultant force at the point and plot it on a lower-hemisphere projection.

The *x*, *y* and *z* Cartesian components of the three forces are given by Equations 6.4; the components of their resultant **r** are found by taking the algebraic sum as follows:

Force	Cartesian components (kN)		
	x	*y*	*z*
u	−2.630	2.368	−6.385
v	−1.223	5.296	2.769
w	8.344	0.583	−9.289
r	4.491	8.247	−12.905

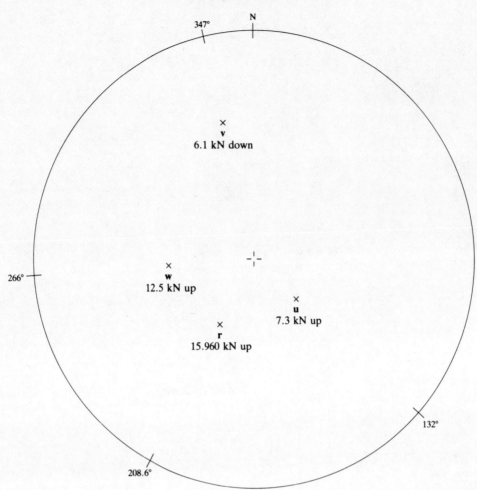

Figure 6.3 The resultant of three forces
(Example 6.3).

The z Cartesian component of the resultant is negative; therefore the force has an upward sense and it is only possible to plot the reverse vector, which, by Equations 6.1 to 6.3 has a magnitude of 15.960 kN, a trend 208.6° and a plunge 54.0°. The forces are plotted in Figure 6.3.

Example 6.4 (Fig. 6.4) The following two forces act at a point:

Force	Trend (deg)	Plunge (deg)	Magnitude (kN)
u	190	60	3
v	095	50	5

Find the trend, plunge, magnitude and sense of the resultant force at the point, for the following combinations of sense of the component forces:

	Sense of force	
	u	**v**
(a)	down	down
(b)	up	up
(c)	up	down
(d)	down	up

Plot the forces on a lower-hemisphere projection.

This example demonstrates the four possible combinations of sense that a given pair of forces could produce; though, of course, only one of these combinations would apply in any particular situation. The x, y and z Cartesian components of the two forces, found from Equations 6.4, and also their resultant **r** for each of the four combinations of sense are listed below. The parameter S is $+1.0$ when the component force has a downward sense and -1.0 when the force is upward.

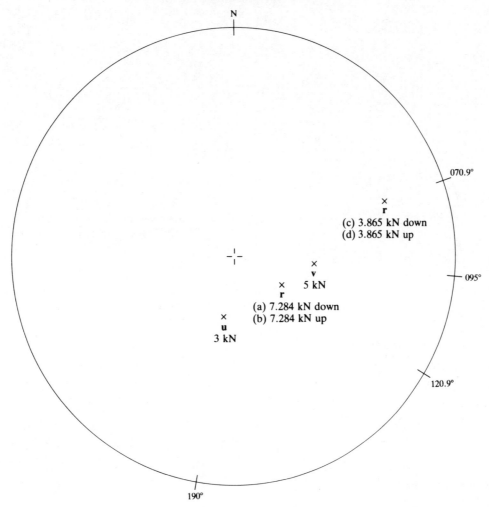

Figure 6.4 The resultant of two forces, with the four possible combinations of sense (Example 6.4).

	Cartesian components (kN)		
Force	x	y	z
u	-0.260 S	-1.477 S	2.598 S
v	3.202 S	-0.280 S	3.830 S
r			
(a)	2.942	-1.757	6.428
(b)	-2.942	1.757	-6.428
(c)	3.462	1.197	1.232
(d)	-3.462	-1.197	-1.232

r	Trend (deg)	Plunge (deg)	Magnitude (kN)	Sense
(a)	120.9	61.9	7.284	down
(b)	120.9	61.9	7.284	up
(c)	070.9	18.6	3.865	down
(d)	070.9	18.6	3.865	up

The forces, which are plotted in Figure 6.4, show that the four possible combinations of sense give rise to two different orientations for the resultant force, with an upward and downward sense for each orientation.

The trend, plunge, magnitude and sense for each of the four different resultant forces are found using Equations 6.1 to 6.3 and listed below. It is important to note that, for combinations (b) and (d) the z Cartesian component of the resultant is negative and hence it has an upward sense, making it necessary to plot the orientation of the reverse vector.

Example 6.5 (Fig. 6.5) The centre of mass of a body weighing 680 kN is acted upon by a horizontal force of 350 kN, with a trend of 241°, the horizontal force being directed towards the south-west. Plot, on a lower-hemisphere projection, the third force that would be required to act through the centre of mass to maintain the body in static equilibrium.

In this example the weight of the body is represented by

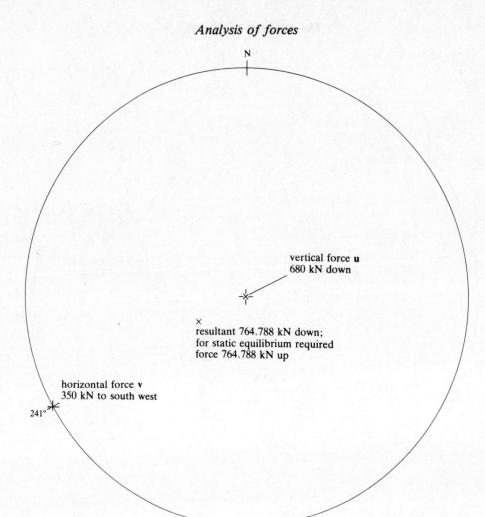

Figure 6.5 Forces in static equilibrium (Example 6.5).

a vertical force **u** of magnitude 680 kN acting downwards through the centre of mass of the body. The x, y and z Cartesian components of the vertical and horizontal forces are given by Equations 6.4 as follows. As before, the Cartesian components of the resultant are found by summing those of the components.

Force	Cartesian components (kN)		
	x	y	z
Vertical **u**	0	0	680
Horizontal **v**	− 306.117	− 169.683	0
Resultant **r**	− 306.117	− 169.683	680

The force required to maintain static equilibrium must have x, y and z Cartesian components of 306.117, 169.683 and − 680.0 kN respectively. This force therefore has an upward sense and it is again necessary to plot the reverse vector, which by Equations 6.1 to 6.3 has a magnitude of 764.788 kN, a trend 241.0° and a plunge 62.8°. The forces are plotted in Figure 6.5.

These examples, and also the exercises at the end of the chapter, serve to illustrate some fundamental principles concerning pairs of forces and their resultant.

(a) A given pair of component forces and their resultant are always coplanar, i.e. they must all lie on the same great circle.

(b) If both component forces have the same sense then the resultant force will plot between them on their common great circle and will also have the same sense as the component forces.

(c) If the component forces are of different sense then the resultant force will not plot between them but will plot somewhere along their external angle on the common great circle.

(d) The resultant of two forces will make a smaller solid angle to the component force with the greater magnitude.

These points may help to minimise the risk of gross errors during the computation and plotting of force vectors.

6.4 Decomposition of a force

6.4.1 Vector algebra method

The decomposition of a force is the inverse of the problem described in the previous section. Consider a known force **r** of trend α_r, plunge β_r, magnitude $|\mathbf{r}|$ and sense S_r. The aim is to split, or decompose, this force into two or more hypothetical components that act through a common point and have **r** as their resultant. There are, in fact, an infinite number of solutions to this problem, since for any arbitrary vector **u** it is always possible to find a vector **v** that gives **r** as their resultant. To provide unique solutions, therefore, it is necessary to give more information about the required component vectors. In rock mechanics applications, this additional information usually takes the form of specified orientations for the required components, leaving their senses and magnitudes as the only unknowns. By using this approach it is possible to decompose a vector into up to three non-parallel components.

It is assumed that the known force **r**, specified above, must be split into three components **u**, **v** and **w**, subject to the requirement that their trends and plunges are respectively α_u, β_u, α_v, β_v, α_w and β_w and also that they act through a common point. The aim is to find the senses and magnitudes of **u**, **v** and **w**. The orientation properties of the three component vectors can be expressed in terms of the Cartesian components of downward-directed unit vectors to which they are parallel. These Cartesian components, which are usually called direction cosines, can be found from Equations 6.4 by setting both the sense and the vector magnitude to unity. The direction cosines for **u** are therefore given by

$$l_x = \sin\alpha_u \cos\beta_u$$
$$l_y = \cos\alpha_u \cos\beta_u \qquad (6.5)$$
$$l_z = \sin\beta_u$$

The direction cosines m_x, m_y and m_z for **v** and n_x, n_y and n_z for **w** can be found in a similar manner. The Cartesian components r_x, r_y and r_z of the known vector **r** can be found from Equations 6.4 in the usual way. If the unknown senses and magnitudes of the component vectors **u**, **v** and **w** are S_u, $|\mathbf{u}|$, S_v, $|\mathbf{v}|$, S_w and $|\mathbf{w}|$ respectively, then Equations 6.4 and 6.5 can be combined to give expressions for the Cartesian components of **u**, **v** and **w**. For example, the x, y and z Cartesian components of **u** are given by

$$u_x = S_u|\mathbf{u}|l_x$$
$$u_y = S_u|\mathbf{u}|l_y$$
$$u_z = S_u|\mathbf{u}|l_z$$

The Cartesian components v_x, v_y and v_z for **v** and w_x, w_y

and w_z for **w** can be specified in a similar manner. It is stipulated that **r** is the resultant of **u**, **v** and **w**; hence, by vector addition

$$\mathbf{r} = \mathbf{u} + \mathbf{v} + \mathbf{w} \qquad (6.6)$$

or, in terms of their Cartesian components

$$r_x = u_x + v_x + w_x$$
$$r_y = u_y + v_y + w_y \qquad (6.7)$$
$$r_z = u_z + v_z + w_z$$

Substituting for the Cartesian components of **u**, **v** and **w** gives

$$r_x = Ul_x + Vm_x + Wn_x$$
$$r_y = Ul_y + Vm_y + Wn_y \qquad (6.8)$$
$$r_z = Ul_z + Vm_z + Wn_z$$

where

$$U = S_u|\mathbf{u}|$$
$$V = S_v|\mathbf{v}| \qquad (6.9)$$
$$W = S_w|\mathbf{w}|$$

The parameters U, V and W, which are the only unknowns in the three simultaneous equations 6.8, can be solved using any convenient algebraic or numerical method. One suitable method is described in Appendix B. The sense and magnitude of each component force can be found from Equations 6.9 by noting that sense takes a value of $+1.0$ for a downward force and -1.0 for an upward force, and that the magnitude of a force is always greater than or equal to zero. Hence the signs of U, V and W indicate the respective senses, while their absolute values give the respective force magnitudes.

In general, a three-dimensional body that is subjected to one or more active forces must be supported by three reactive forces to give a statically determinate structure. As before, it is assumed that all forces act through the same point. The orientations of the reactive forces, which are dictated only by the orientations of the supports, can be specified in terms of their trends and plunges or in terms of their direction cosines as explained above. Suppose that the resultant of the active forces on the body is **r**, and that the unknown reactive forces are given by the vectors **a**, **b** and **c** directed along the specified reaction orientations. If the body is in static equilibrium, then the resultant of the active and reactive forces must be zero, i.e.

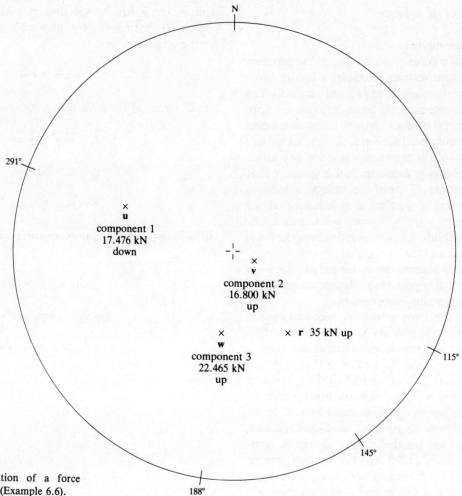

Figure 6.6 Decomposition of a force into three components (Example 6.6).

$$r + a + b + c = 0$$

or

$$r = -a - b - c$$

Comparision of the above expression with Equation 6.6 shows that the reactive forces can be obtained by finding the components of **r** along the three specified reaction orientations and then simply taking the reverse, or negative, vectors.

Example 6.6 (Fig. 6.6) A force of magnitude 35 kN acts in an upward sense along a line of trend 145° and plunge 43°. Find the magnitudes and senses of the components of this force that act along lines with the following trends/plunges: (1) 291/34, (2) 115/78, (3) 188/50.

Here it is assumed that **r** corresponds to the known force of magnitude 35 kN and that **u**, **v** and **w** are the three unknown components 1, 2 and 3 respectively, whose orientations have been given. The Cartesian components of **r** are found from Equations 6.4; the direction cosines of **u**, **v** and **w** are found using equations such as 6.5. These

Cartesian components and direction cosines are substituted in Equations 6.8 to give the following simultaneous equations:

$$-14.682 = -0.774U + 0.188V - 0.089W$$

$$20.968 = 0.297U - 0.088V - 0.637W$$

$$-23.870 = 0.559U + 0.978V + 0.766W$$

where the unknown values U, V and W give the senses and magnitudes of the component forces, according to Equations 6.9. Solution of the above simultaneous equations using the methods explained in Appendix B gives the following results:

$$U = 17.476 \, \text{kN} \qquad V = -16.800 \, \text{kN} \qquad W = -22.465 \, \text{kN}$$

The signs of these values indicate that the first component has a downward sense, and that the other two components have an upward sense, as shown in Figure 6.6.

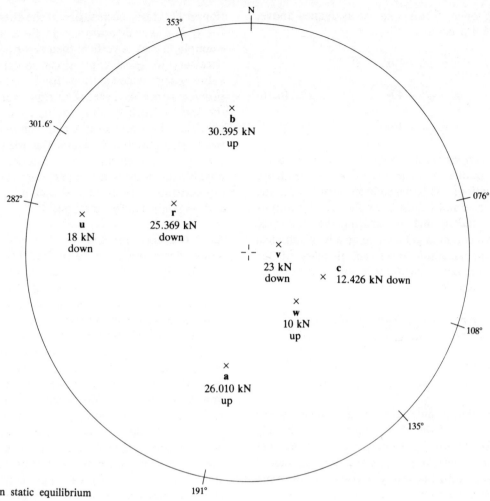

Figure 6.7 Forces in static equilibrium (Example 6.7).

Example 6.7 (Fig. 6.7) Three forces **u**, **v** and **w**, which act at a point P in a small weightless body, have the following properties:

Force	Trend (deg)	Plunge (deg)	Magnitude (kN)	Sense
u	282	15	18	down
v	076	74	23	down
w	135	56	10	up

The body is supported in static equilibrium by three reactive forces **a**, **b** and **c** that act through the point P along lines with trends/plunges 191/36, 353/25 and 108/51 respectively. Find the magnitudes and senses of the three reactions.

The resultant **r** of the three active forces **u**, **v** and **w** is found using the method described earlier and also in Example 6.3. This resultant has a trend 301.6°, plunge 46.7°, magnitude 25.369 kN and a downward sense. This force can now be decomposed into three components with orientations parallel to the reactive forces **a**, **b** and **c**. The properties of these components are as follows:

Force	Trend (deg)	Plunge (deg)	Magnitude (kN)	Sense Component	Sense Reaction
a	191	36	26.010	down	up
b	353	25	30.395	down	up
c	108	51	12.426	up	down

The properties of the reactive forces **a**, **b** and **c** are the same as those of the components, except that they have the opposite sense, as listed above and also shown in Figure 6.7. The resultant of the three active forces **u**, **v** and **w** and the three reactions **a**, **b** and **c** has zero magnitude; this confirms that the body is in static equilibrium.

If the known force **r** is to be decomposed into only two

non-parallel component forces **u** and **v**, as defined above, then Equations 6.8 become

$$r_x = Ul_x + Vm_x$$

$$r_y = Ul_y + Vm_y \qquad (6.10)$$

$$r_z = Ul_z + Vm_z$$

These three equations contain only two unknown values U and V, which implies that there is a linear dependence between the equations. This dependence arises from the requirement that **r**, **u** and **v** must be coplanar. This important requirement can be met by ensuring that the three forces all plot on a common great circle on a hemispherical projection. Simple algebraic inversion of pairs of the expressions for r_x, r_y and r_z yields three alternative expressions for U and three for V as follows

$$U = \frac{r_x m_y - r_y m_x}{l_x m_y - l_y m_x} = \frac{r_y m_z - r_z m_y}{l_y m_z - l_z m_y} = \frac{r_z m_x - r_x m_z}{l_z m_x - l_x m_z}$$

$$V = \frac{l_x r_y - l_y r_x}{l_x m_y - l_y m_x} = \frac{l_y r_z - l_z r_y}{l_y m_z - l_z m_y} = \frac{l_z r_x - l_x r_z}{l_z m_x - l_x m_z} \qquad (6.11)$$

In general, and if **r**, **u** and **v** are coplanar but non-zero and non-parallel, any of the above expressions will yield solutions for U and V, which are interpreted in the manner described earlier. There are, however, certain special orientations of **r**, **u** and **v** that can give rise to one or more zero values in the numerators and denominators of Equa-

tions 6.11. If this occurs, one of the alternative expressions for U and V will always yield the correct solution. for example, if **r** were vertical then $r_x = r_y = 0$ and it would be necessary to select expressions containing the non-zero value r_z to provide solutions for U and V. A more serious problem concerning the use of Equations 6.11 occurs when the specified orientations for **r**, **u** and **v** are not exactly coplanar. This difficulty, which can arise when graphical methods are used to determine the orientations of **u** and **v**, can lead to significant errors. Consequently, unless it is possible to ensure that **r**, **u** and **v** are coplanar, the following alternative graphical approach offers a more accurate, and certainly quicker method.

6.4.2 Graphical method

When decomposing a force into two components, the requirement that the three forces involved are coplanar can be met approximately by ensuring that they all plot on a common great circle on a hemispherical projection. Angular measurements taken along this great circle lead to a direct, and relatively simple, method for evaluating the magnitudes and senses of the two component forces. This method has the advantage of giving satisfactory results even when the three forces are not exactly coplanar. It is first necessary to plot the orientations of the known force **r**, and also the first component force **u**, as points on the projection. It can be helpful, at this stage, to annotate the point representing **r** to indicate the magnitude and sense of the force. The second component force **v** must plot somewhere along the great circle containing **r** and **u** to ensure coplanarity. It is now important to recognise that three different general situations can arise, depending upon which of the forces plots between the other two. A point plots between two others if it lies somewhere along their internal angle on the projection. The three different situations are as follows.

(a)

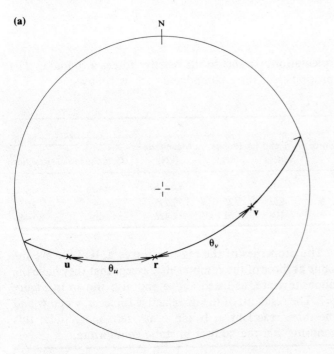

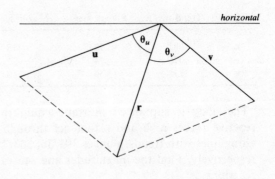

Figure 6.8 Angular measurements for the decomposition of a force into two components.

(b)

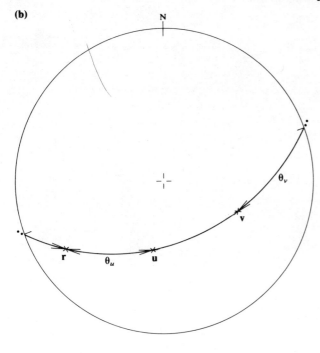

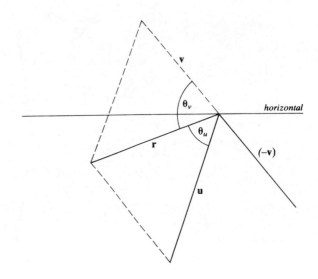

(c)

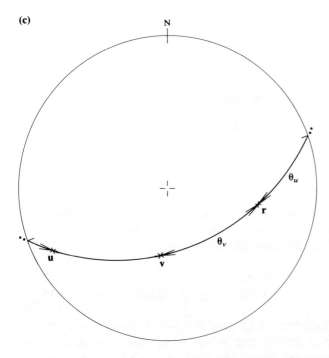

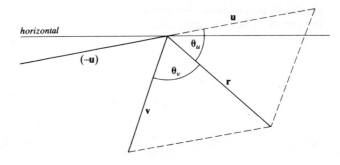

Figure 6.8 *Cont.*

(a) **r** plots between **u** and **v** (Fig. 6.8a): In this case **u** and **v** both have the same sense as **r**. The angle θ_u is measured internally between **u** and **r**; the angle θ_v is measured internally between **v** and **r**.

(b) **u** plots between **r** and **v** (Fig. 6.8b): In this case **u** has the same sense as **r** but **v** has the opposite sense to **r**. The angle θ_u is measured internally between **u** and **r**; the angle θ_v is measured externally between **v** and **r**.

(c) **v** plots between **u** and **r** (Fig. 6.8c): In this final case **v** has the same sense as **r** but **u** has the opposite sense to **r**. The angle θ_u is measured externally between **u**

and **r**; the angle θ_v is measured internally between **v** and **r**.

A simple way of remembering these rules is to ensure that the angles θ_u and θ_v are measured either internally or externally to **r** so that *they do not overlap*. An internal angle is always associated with a component of the same sense as **r**; an external angle is associated with a component that has the opposite sense to **r**. In all cases $\theta_u + \theta_v \leqslant 180°$, and the magnitudes of **u** and **v** are found by using the sine rule to solve the parallelograms of forces in Figure 6.8:

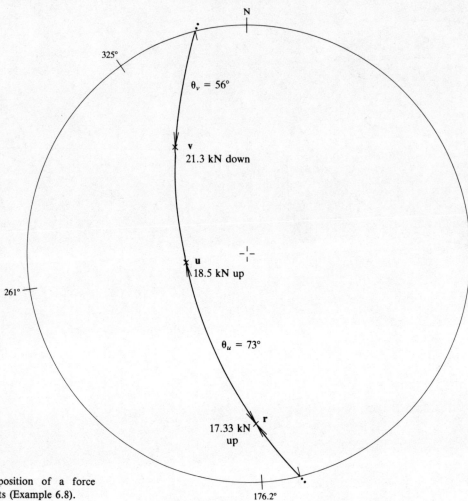

Figure 6.9 Decomposition of a force into two components (Example 6.8).

$$|\mathbf{u}| = \frac{|\mathbf{r}| \sin\theta_v}{\sin(\theta_u + \theta_v)} \qquad (6.12)$$

$$|\mathbf{v}| = \frac{|\mathbf{r}| \sin\theta_u}{\sin(\theta_u + \theta_v)} \qquad (6.13)$$

Finally, if the angle between **u** and **v** is 90°, it is permissible to decompose either **u** or **v** into two further components. If **u** is selected for further decomposition, this must occur in the plane that has **v** as its normal. Similarly, if **v** is selected, decomposition occurs in the plane that has **u** as its normal.

Example 6.8 (Fig. 6.9) A force of magnitude 17.33 kN acts in an upward sense along a line of approximate trend 176.2° and plunge 16.3°. Find the magnitudes and senses of the components of this force that act along lines with the trends/plunges (1) 261/59, (2) 325/31, which are coplanar with **r**.

Again **r** corresponds to the force of known magnitude 17.33 kN and **u** and **v** are the unknown components whose orientations are given. The Cartesian components of **r** are $r_x = -1.102$, $r_y = 16.597$, $r_z = -4.864$.

The direction cosines of **u** and **v** are

$$l_x = -0.509 \qquad l_y = -0.081 \qquad l_z = 0.857$$
$$m_x = -0.492 \qquad m_y = 0.702 \qquad m_z = 0.515$$

Equations 6.11 give $U \simeq -18.6$ kN and $V \simeq 21.5$ kN, which implies that **u** has an upward sense and **v** has a downward sense. The approximate nature of the answer derives from rounding errors in the specification of the trend and plunge of **r**.

Figure 6.9 illustrates the graphical method for decomposing the force in this example. The component **u** plots between **r** and **v**, and consequently **u** has the same upward sense as **r** but **v** has the opposite (i.e. downward) sense. The angle θ_u is measured internally as 73°; θ_v is measured externally as 56°. From Equations 6.12 and 6.13 $|\mathbf{u}| = 18.5$ kN and $|\mathbf{v}| = 21.3$ kN, which, allowing for the fact that the angles θ_u and θ_v were measured off to the nearest degree, agrees with the earlier result.

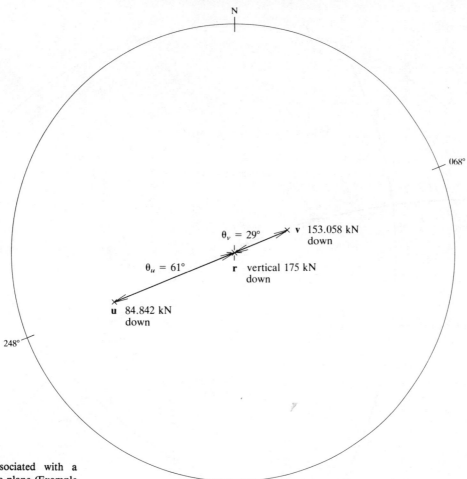

Figure 6.10 Forces associated with a block resting on a single plane (Example 6.9).

Example 6.9 (Fig. 6.10) A block of rock weighing 175 kN rests on a planar slope that has a dip direction 248° and a dip amount 29°. Calculate the magnitudes and senses of the components of the block weight that act (1) along the line of maximum dip of the slope, and (2) along the normal to the slope.

Here **r** corresponds to the vertical weight vector, which has a downward sense. The line of maximum dip of the slope, represented by **u**, has a trend 248° and plunge 29°. The normal to the slope, represented by **v**, has a trend of 068° (i.e 248 − 180) and a plunge of 61° (i.e. 90 − 29). Figure 6.10 shows that **r** plots between the components **u** and **v**; this means that these components both have the same downward sense as **r**, and that the angles θ_u and θ_v are both measured internally to **r**. These angles can be either measured from the projection or, since in this case **r**, **u** and **v** lie in a vertical plane, calculated from the appropriate values of plunge. The resulting values of θ_u and θ_v, which are 61° and 29° respectively, are input to Equations 6.12 and 6.13 to give $|\mathbf{u}| = 84.842$ kN, $|\mathbf{v}| = 153.058$ kN. This type of problem, which occurs quite frequently in rock mechanics studies, lends itself to a direct non-graphical solution. In the particular case where **r** is *vertical* and plots between **u** and **v**, and where the angles $\theta_u + \theta_v = 90°$, Equations 6.12 and 6.13 reduce to

$$|\mathbf{u}| = |\mathbf{r}| \sin \beta_u$$
$$|\mathbf{v}| = |\mathbf{r}| \cos \beta_u \qquad (6.14)$$

where β_u is the plunge of **u**. In this case both **u** and **v** have the same sense as **r**.

If required, either **u** or **v** could be decomposed further since, in this case, the components are at right angles to each other. This is illustrated in the next example. Before leaving this example it is worth emphasising that **u** and **v** are components of the weight vector **r**. The reactions, chosen parallel to **u** and **v** to maintain static equilibrium with **r**, have the same magnitudes but are of the opposite sense to these components.

Example 6.10 (Fig. 6.11) A wedge-shaped block of rock weighing 836 kN rests on two planes that have dip directions/dip amounts as follows: (a) 148/54, (b) 251/42.

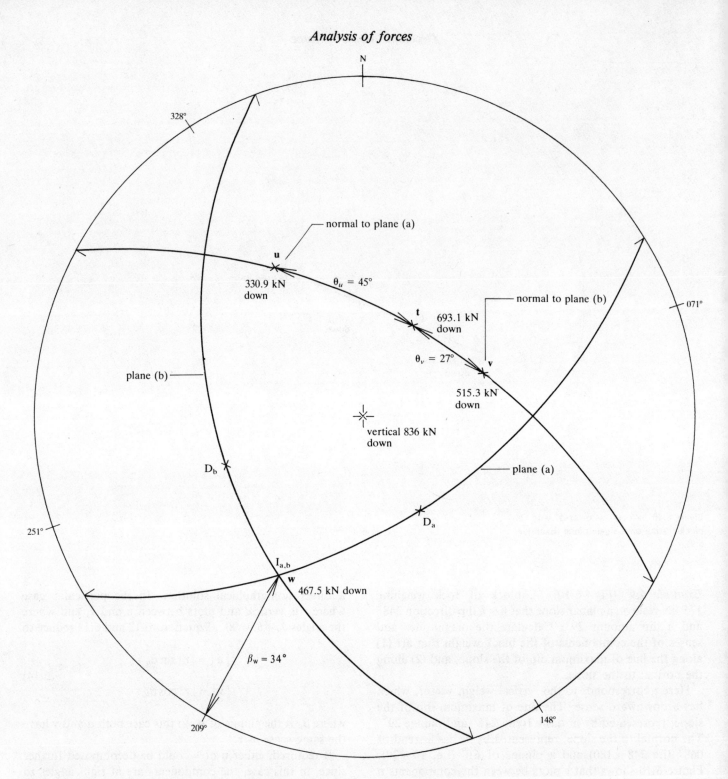

normal to plane (a)

u

330.9 kN
down

$\theta_u = 45°$

t 693.1 kN
down

normal to plane (b)

$\theta_v = 27°$

v

071°

515.3 kN
down

plane (b)

vertical 836 kN
down

plane (a)

D$_b$

D$_a$

251°

I$_{a,b}$

w 467.5 kN down

$\beta_w = 34°$

209°

148°

328°

Figure 6.11 Forces associated with a wedge-shaped block resting on two planes (Example 6.10).

Calculate the magnitudes and senses of the components of the block weight that act (1) along the normal to plane (a), (2) along the normal to plane (b), and (3) along the line of intersection of the two planes. Assume that all forces act through the centre of mass of the block.

Again **r** corresponds to the vertical weight vector, which has a downward sense. The normal to plane (a) represented by **u** has a trend 328° and plunge 36°; the normal to plane (b) represented by **v** has a trend 071° and plunge 48°. Figure 6.11 shows that the line of intersection between planes (a) and (b), represented by **w**, has a trend 209° and a plunge 34°, measured to the nearest degree.

The problem can be solved using the vector methods explained earlier in this chapter. Substitution of the values

64

for the Cartesian components of **r** and the direction cosines of **u**, **v** and **w** into Equations 6.8 yields the following simultaneous equations:

$$0 = -0.429U + 0.633V - 0.402W$$
$$0 = 0.686U + 0.218V - 0.725W$$
$$836 = 0.588U + 0.743V + 0.559W$$

Solution of these simultaneous equations using the methods explained in Appendix B gives the following results:

$$U = 327.0 \text{ kN} \qquad V = 516.7 \text{ kN} \qquad W = 464.6 \text{ kN}$$

Hence the component that is normal to plane (a) is 327.0 kN, the component normal to plane (b) is 516.7 kN and the component along the line of intersection is 464.6 kN. All of these components have the same downward sense as the weight vector **r**. As before, the reactions, chosen parallel to **u**, **v** and **w** to maintain static equilibrium with **r**, have the same magnitudes but are of the opposite sense to the respective components.

The type of problem illustrated in the above example frequently occurs during stability analyses of sliding mechanisms for wedge-shaped rigid rock blocks. This particular geometry lends itself well to a simplified graphical analysis for determining the component forces, which obviates the need for the somewhat lengthy vector methods. In order to apply the graphical methods, it is first necessary to recognise that, in this case, **u** and **v** lie in a plane whose normal is parallel to **w** (see Section 3.5). It is therefore possible first to decompose **r** into two components **w** and **t**, where the orientation of **t** is selected so that it is at right angles to **w** and also coplanar with **w** and **r**. Because **t** is at right angles to **w** it must be coplanar with **u** and **v**. The component **t** can therefore be decomposed further to give the components **u** and **v**.

In the first stage of the decomposition, **r** plots between **w** and **t**, so the two components have the same downward sense as **r**. In addition, since **w** and **t** are at right angles, Equations 6.14 can be applied to find the magnitudes of the component forces. In this case

$$|\mathbf{w}| = |\mathbf{r}| \sin \beta_w$$

and

$$|\mathbf{t}| = |\mathbf{r}| \cos \beta_w$$

where β_w, which is 34° in the above example, is the plunge of **w**. Hence $|\mathbf{w}| = 467.5$ kN and $|\mathbf{t}| = 693.1$ kN. In the second stage of decomposition **t** again plots between **u** and **v** so the two components have the same downward sense

as **t**. The angles θ_u and θ_v are measured internally to **t** and are 45° and 27° respectively. Applying Equations 6.12 and 6.13 gives $|\mathbf{u}| = 330.9$ kN and $|\mathbf{v}| = 515.3$ kN. In the geotechnical context, the reduction in precision associated with the graphical approach is more than compensated, in this particular type of problem, by the relative ease of computation.

In the wedge analysis described above, **r** will always plot between **w** and **t**, so these two components always have the same downward sense as the weight vector **r**. It is quite possible, however, for the two planes (a) and (b) to be of such an orientation that **t** does not plot between **u** and **v**. If this occurs, either **u** or **v** will have the opposite (i.e. upward) sense to **t**. This implies that, unless the plane carrying the upward normal force overhangs the block, the plane will be subjected to a tensile normal force. It is usual practice in rock mechanics studies to assume that discontinuity planes cannot sustain a tensile normal force. In view of this it would be necessary to reanalyse the forces on the assumption that the weight of the block is carried completely on the other single plane. This problem will be discussed further in the next chapter.

6.5 The scalar and vector products

The scalar product of two vectors **u** and **v** is usually written **u.v** and defined as follows

$$\mathbf{u}.\mathbf{v} = |\mathbf{u}| \, |\mathbf{v}| \cos \theta$$

where θ ($< 180°$) is the angle between the positive directions of **u** and **v**. The scalar product can be determined from the Cartesian components of **u** and **v** as follows

$$\mathbf{u}.\mathbf{v} = u_x v_x + u_y v_y + u_z v_z$$

The scalar product, which provides a convenient method for calculating the angle between two lines, was used to obtain Equation 3.1. Chapter 3 also contains a hemispherical projection method for finding the angle between two lines.

The vector product of two vectors **u** and **v** is usually written $\mathbf{u} \times \mathbf{v}$ and is a vector of magnitude $|\mathbf{u}| \, |\mathbf{v}| \sin \theta$ where again θ ($< 180°$) is the angle between the positive directions of **u** and **v**. The vector product is a vector **i**, with x, y and z Cartesian components $(u_y v_z - u_z v_y)$, $(u_z v_x - u_x v_z)$, $(u_x v_y - u_y v_x)$ respectively, which acts along a line that is normal to the plane containing **u** and **v**. The positive direction of **i** is given by the drive direction of a left-hand[2] screw rotated through the angle θ from **u** to **v**. The physical interpretation of the vector product is that if **u** and **v** are the normals to a pair of intersecting planes,

[2] This is because a left-handed Cartesian coordinate system has been used.

65

then their vector product **i** is parallel to the line of intersection of the planes. Section 3.5, which deals with intersecting planes, therefore provides an alternative, hemispherical projection method for finding the orientation of a vector product.

When vectors are used to analyse only orientation properties, it is generally convenient to operate with vectors of unit magnitude aligned parallel to the features of interest. Example 3.5 concerns the intersection between plane 1, of dip direction/dip amount 146/59, and plane 2, of dip direction/dip amount 266/36. Downward-directed unit vectors **u** and **v**, normal to planes 1 and 2, have Cartesian components (direction cosines) −0.479, 0.711, 0.515 and 0.586, 0.041, 0.809 respectively, found using Equations 6.5. The scalar product of **u** and **v** is 0.165, which is the cosine of the angle between the normals to planes 1 and 2. This angle is therefore 80.5° which agrees approximately with the value of 81° found graphically in Example 3.5. The Cartesian components of the vector product $\mathbf{i} = \mathbf{u} \times \mathbf{v}$ are 0.554, 0.690, −0.436. This vector acts with an upward sense along a line that has a trend 218.8° and a plunge 26.3°. This result again agrees approximately with the orientation of the line of intersection, 219/26, found graphically in Example 3.5.

6.6 The friction cone

Planar discontinuities in a rock mass can become planes of failure when the forces acting on them take on certain critical values. One of the simplest models for this behaviour is based upon the normal and shear components of the resultant force **r** (and its reaction −**r**) acting at a point on the plane. The normal component **n** (and its reaction −**n**) acts normal to the plane in question. The shear component **s** (and its reaction −**s**) is parallel to the discontinuity plane and also lies in the plane containing **r** and **n**, as shown in Figure 6.12. The group of forces **r**, −**n** and −**s** are in static equilibrium, as are the forces −**r**, **n** and **s**.

Because **n** and **s** are at right angles, decomposition of **r** is relatively straightforward. If θ is the acute solid angle between **r** and the normal to the plane then

$$|\mathbf{n}| = |\mathbf{r}| \cos \theta \qquad (6.15)$$

and

$$|\mathbf{s}| = |\mathbf{r}| \sin \theta \qquad (6.16)$$

It is assumed that the discontinuity will remain stable as long as the following conditions are satisfied:

(a) The normal forces **n** and −**n** must form a compressive pair across the plane.
(b) The magnitude of the shear component $|\mathbf{s}|$ must be less than $|\mathbf{n}| \tan \phi$, where ϕ is the angle of friction for the discontinuity plane.

The first condition, which assumes that the discontinuity has zero tensile strength, can be tested by examining the sense of **r**. Combining Equations 6.15 and 6.16 with the second condition gives the requirement that, for stability $\sin \theta < \cos \theta \tan \phi$, or $\theta < \phi$. This simple result suggests that if a locus of cone angle ϕ is constructed, on the projection, about the point representing the discontinuity normal, the second condition for stability will always be satisfied if **r** plots anywhere within the locus. If **r** plots outside the locus, and the normal forces are compressive, shear failure will occur in the direction of **s**. This locus of cone angle ϕ is usually referred to as the friction cone.

Example 6.11 (Fig. 6.13) A block of rock weighing 140 kN has a planar base and rests on a non-overhanging planar slope of dip direction/dip amount 253/39. A cable force of magnitude T and a downward sense acts through the centre of mass of the block along a line of trend 110° and plunge 20°. If the interface between the block and the slope has a friction angle of 30°, determine the range of values of T that maintain the block in a stable condition with respect to sliding failure.

The first step in this problem is to plot the normal, N_f, and the great circle of the planar slope on a hemispherical projection. A locus with a cone angle of 30° is then constructed about the slope normal N_f, following one of the methods explained in Section 4.2. This is the friction cone.

The vector **u** represents the vertical weight of the block, of magnitude 140 kN, and the vector **v** represents the cable force of known orientation and downward sense but of unknown magnitude $|\mathbf{v}| = T$. Because **u** and **v** both act downwards on the block, the interface between its base

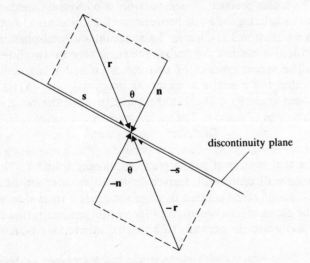

Figure 6.12 Forces acting on a discontinuity plane.

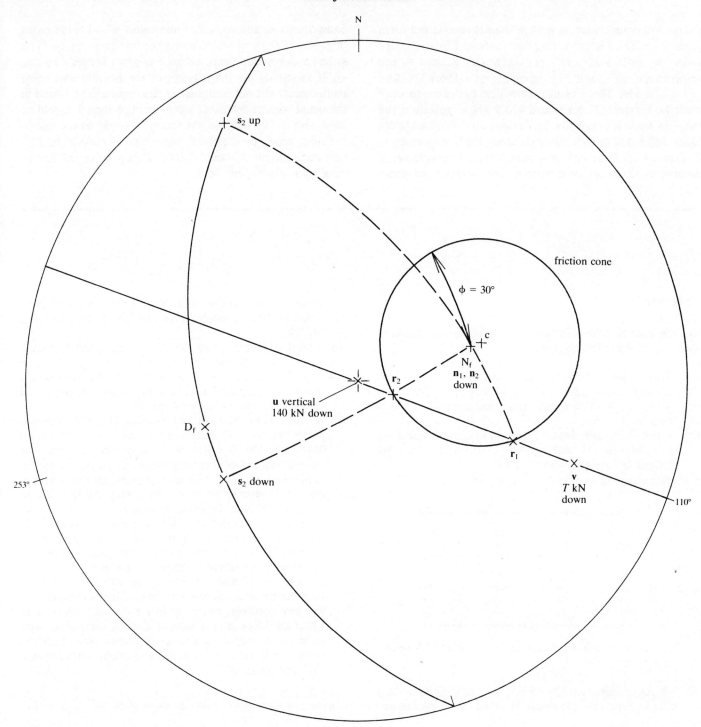

Figure 6.13 The friction cone (Example 6.11).

and the slope is maintained in compression; consequently the only feasible mode of failure is by sliding. The block will just begin to slide when the resultant of **u** and **v** plots on the friction cone. Because this resultant must be coplanar with **u** and **v** it can only lie at one of two points on the friction cone, labelled **r₁** and **r₂** in Figure 6.13. Both of these resultants plot between **u** and **v** and therefore offer valid possibilities, both with a downward sense. It is

important to consider the validity of a hypothetical resultant force in this way, bearing in mind the principles outlined at the end of Section 6.3. For example, if **v** had plotted between **u** and **r₁** then **u** and **v** would have to have a different sense from each other to give **r₁** as a valid resultant.

For **r₁**, the angles θ_u and θ_v in Equations 6.12 and 6.13, measured from the projection, are 54° and 16° respectively. Applying Equation 6.12 in slightly rearranged form gives $|\mathbf{r}_1| = 477.3$ kN. Putting this value in Equation 6.13 gives $|\mathbf{v}| = 410.9$ kN. For $\mathbf{r}_2$, the angles θ_u and θ_v are respectively $13°$ and $57°$, giving $|\mathbf{r}_2| = 156.9$ kN and $|\mathbf{v}| = 37.6$ kN, These results show that the cable force T must lie between 37.6 kN and 410.9 kN to maintain the block in a stable condition. If T is just above 410.9 kN the block will begin to slide upwards along the line given by $\mathbf{s}_1$ in Figure 6.13. The vector $\mathbf{s}_1$ must have an upward sense because $\mathbf{r}_1$ does not plot between the normal and shear components $\mathbf{n}_1$ and $\mathbf{s}_1$. If T is just below 37.6 kN the block begins to slide downwards along the line given by $\mathbf{s}_2$. Here $\mathbf{s}_2$ has a downward sense because $\mathbf{r}_2$ plots between $\mathbf{n}_2$ and $\mathbf{s}_2$. If required, the magnitudes of the normal and shear components at both limiting conditions could be found in the usual way. If the cable were removed then T would be zero, and the vertical weight vector $\mathbf{u}$ would be the resultant force acting on the block. Since $\mathbf{u}$ plots outside the friction cone the block would fail by sliding down the line of maximum dip of the slope.

Exercises

The Cartesian co-ordinate system shown in Figure 6.1 should be used for all of the following exercises.

6.1 The x, y and z Cartesian components of two force vectors are respectively (i) 4.9, -12.3, 8.8 kN and (ii) -24.7, 16.5, -30.2 kN. Find the trend, plunge, magnitude and sense of each force vector.

6.2 A force of magnitude 51.9 kN acts in an upward sense along a line of trend $133°$ and plunge $38°$. Determine the x, y and z Cartesian components of this force.

6.3 The following four forces act at a point:

Trend (deg)	Plunge (deg)	Magnitude (kN)	Sense
229	16	12.4	up
106	79	28.6	down
153	51	16.3	down
317	44	9.7	up

Find the trend, plunge, magnitude and sense of the resultant force at the point.

6.4 A force of magnitude 135 kN acts in an upward sense along a line of trend $163°$ and plunge $58°$. Find the magnitudes and senses of the components of this force that act along lines with the following trends/plunges: (i) 066/23, (ii) 108/61, (iii) 242/35.

6.5 A block of rock weighing 200 kN rests on a planar slope that has a dip direction/dip amount 164/36. Calculate the magnitudes and senses of the reactions to the block weight that act (i) along the line of maximum dip of the slope, and (ii) along the normal to the slope.

6.6 A wedge-shaped block of rock weighing 425 kN rests on two planes that have dip directions/dip amounts as follows: (a) 233/41, (b) 329/50. Calculate the magnitudes and senses of the reactions to the block weight that act (i) along the normal to plane (a), (ii) along the normal to plane (b), and (iii) along the line of intersection of the two planes. Assume that all forces act through the centre of mass of the block.

6.7 A block of rock weighing 85 kN has a planar base and rests on a non-overhanging planar slope of dip direction/dip amount 162/43. A cable force of magnitude T and a downward sense acts through the centre of mass of the block along a line of trend $330°$ and plunge $60°$. If the interface between the block and the slope has a friction angle of $27°$, and zero cohesion, determine (i) the critical value of T at which the block is in a state of limiting equilibrium with respect to sliding failure, and (ii) this critical value of T if the cable were to act in a downward sense along a line of trend $342°$ and plunge $20°$.

Answers to these exercises are given on page 123.

7 Kinematic analysis of rigid blocks by inclined hemisphere projection methods

7.1 Introduction

The stability of a discontinuous rock mass exposed at a free face, for example at a slope or in an underground excavation, is in many cases controlled by the orientation, geometry and strength of the more extensive discontinuities within the mass. If these discontinuities are sufficiently large and frequent, they can combine to form separate blocks that could perhaps fall, or, if unstable, slide from the free face (Fig. 7.1). It is often found that near a free face, particularly in relatively shallow excava-

tions, the *in situ* stresses are small compared with the deformability of the rock material. In such cases blocks of rock within the mass do not deform significantly on exposure and rarely break; this allows them to be treated as effectively rigid bodies in any stability analysis.

Prior to designing a surface or underground excavation in a discontinuous rock mass, it is of vital importance to investigate the relevant geometrical and mechanical properties of discontinuities in the rock adjacent to the proposed excavation. This allows an assessment to be made of the stability of rigid rock blocks that could be exposed during excavation. Methods for the measurement and analysis of discontinuity orientation data have been explained in Chapters 4 and 5. Methods for measuring the frequency and size of discontinuities have been explained by Priest and Hudson (1976, 1981) and by Hudson and Priest (1983). Techniques for measuring other geometrical properties and also the shear strengths of discontinuities have been explained by Hoek and Bray (1981) and Brady and Brown (1985). When the necessary data have been collected, the first stage in any stability analysis is to define the geometry of a potentially unstable rigid block. A failure mechanism can then be postulated, the relevant forces can be analysed and then finally the stability can be determined.

In this chapter and the next only two simple block failure mechanisms will be considered: movement through free air and simple translational sliding. Blocks that undergo the sliding mechanism are assumed to slide either on a single plane or alternatively on a pair of adjacent planes along their line of intersection. The more complex mechanisms involving toppling and rotation are beyond the scope of this book. The interested reader should consult the texts by Wittke (1965) and Thompson (1983) for detailed discussions and analyses of these mechanisms.

In three dimensions, at least four planes are required to delimit a block. When only four planes are involved, the resulting block is a tetrahedron, as shown in Figure 7.2. One side of the tetrahedron is formed by the rock face; the other three sides are formed by non-parallel discontinuity planes, or perhaps other free faces. This, the simplest of all block geometries, is common in rock masses where there are three or more mutually inclined discontinuity orientations. The work in this chapter will be confined to the analysis of tetrahedral blocks that have at least one side

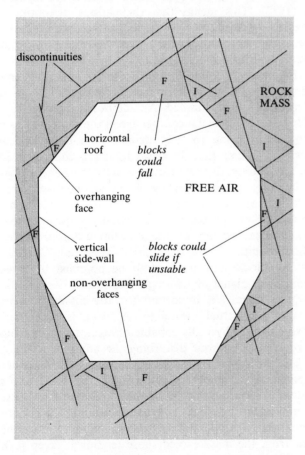

Key

F kinematically feasible tetrahedral blocks
I kinematically infeasible blocks

Figure 7.1 Blocks formed at overhanging and non-overhanging free faces.

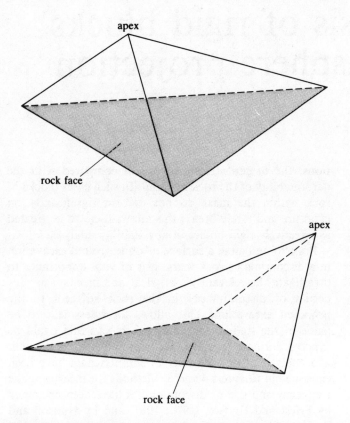

apex

rock face

apex

rock face

Figure 7.2 Typical tetrahedral block geometries.

formed by a planar rock face. More complex polyhedra are discussed by Priest (1980), Warburton (1981) and Goodman and Shi (1984).

7.2 Kinematic feasibility and kinematic congruence

For all practical purposes, it is convenient to assume that a given free face of an excavation is a planar feature that divides the three-dimensional space in its vicinity into two half-spaces: one made of rock, the other of free air. Non-planar, cylindrical faces have been discussed by Priest (1980) and will not be considered in this chapter. In addition to specifying the orientation of a given planar face, it is also necessary to state on which side of the face the rock mass lies. For a non-vertical face this can be achieved by specifying whether the face is overhanging or not. If an imaginary point, moving downwards along a vertical line that passes through the face, travels from rock to free air, then the face is overhanging; if the imaginary point travels downwards from free air to rock then the face is non-overhanging (Fig. 7.1). The roofs of excavations and hanging walls in mines are overhanging faces; rock slopes and foot walls in mines are usually non-overhanging. If the face is vertical it is necessary to specify on which side of the face the rock lies, by means of some other convenient method. In most cases it is obvious, from

the geometry of a proposed excavation, on which side of a given face the rock mass will lie.

The following simple illustration will be used to introduce some principles that are fundamental to the analysis of rigid block failures at planar faces. It is assumed that an investigation of the discontinuity characteristics of a given rock mass has shown that there are three sets of planar discontinuities, of sufficient frequency and size to pose a threat of rigid, tetrahedral block failures at the free faces of a proposed excavation. No matter how exhaustive the site investigation has been, there is no way of knowing the precise location of each individual discontinuity until the excavation is under way. In order to formulate a preliminary design it is necessary, therefore, to make some assumptions about the locations of individual discontinuities. One simple approach is to make the conservative assumption that each discontinuity will occur at a location so that, with other discontinuities, it defines the largest and potentially least stable tetrahedral block. This approach is similar to the 'ubiquitous joint method' described by Cartney (1977). This means that the various discontinuity planes are assumed to be positioned, at their correct orientations, so that together with a given free face they define potentially critical blocks.

It is sometimes found that one or more additional free faces, not parallel to the main face, occur in the vicinity of the rock mass being studied. An additional free face can, under certain circumstances, behave in the same way as a discontinuity plane to help delimit potentially critical blocks at the main face. In view of this it is convenient to treat any additional free faces in exactly the same way as discontinuity planes, bearing in mind, however, that blocks cannot exist on the free air side of any additional free face. This approach, which implicitly assumes that any additional free face has the same ubiquitous properties as discontinuities, is discussed further in Section 7.4. Until then, all blocks are assumed to be bounded by three discontinuity planes and a single free face.

At this stage it is important to differentiate between potential and actual instability. A block is potentially unstable if it is physically capable of being removed from the rock mass without disturbing the adjacent rock. A block of this type is said to be kinematically feasible since its potential instability is assessed on the basis of its freedom to move and not upon the forces that may cause this movement. A block is actually unstable if it is both kinematically feasible and the forces tending to move the block from the mass exceed those tending to keep it in place. These ideas are illustrated in Figure 7.1.

It is possible to position any three mutually intersecting, non-parallel discontinuity planes in only two different spatial arrangements at any overhanging or non-overhanging rock face. If this face is not parallel to any of the discontinuity planes involved, one arrangement always produces a kinematically feasible tetrahedral block; the

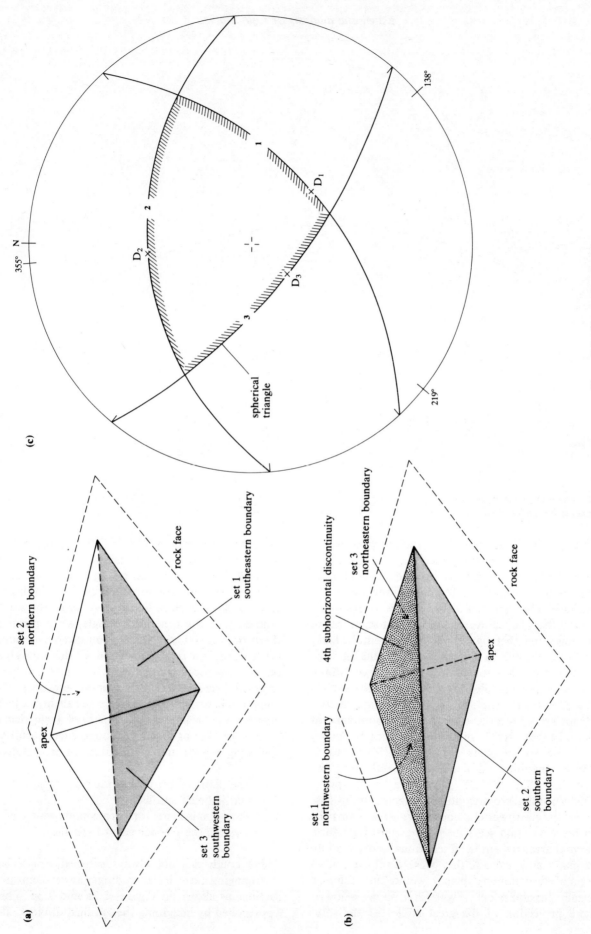

Figure 7.3 Kinematic congruence.

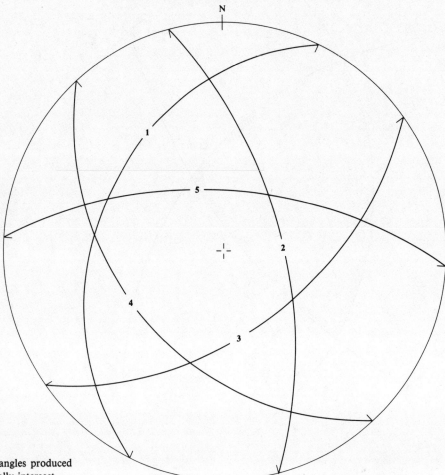

Figure 7.4 Spherical triangles produced by five planes that mutually intersect.

other arrangement does not. The initial problem is, therefore, to discover the arrangement, or more precisely the relative locations, of groups of three discontinuity planes that define kinematically feasible tetrahedral blocks at a given face. This can be achieved simply by arranging the planes so that they converge to a point somewhere in the rock mass and thereby delimit a tetrahedral block. Consider, for example, a horizontal, overhanging rock face intersected by three persistent, planar discontinuity sets with the following dip directions/dip amounts: (1) 138/51, (2) 355/40 and (3) 219/67. In Figure 7.3a, a discontinuity from set 1 forms the southeastern boundary of a tetrahedral block, set 2 forms the northern boundary and set 3 the southwestern boundary. This block is kinematically feasible and could easily fall from the horizontal face. Figure 7.3b shows the other spatial arrangement of the three discontinuity planes. In this case set 1 forms the northwestern boundary, set 2 forms the southern boundary and set 3 the northeastern boundary. In this second arrangement the discontinuities diverge into the rock mass and, even if they were cut by a fourth subhorizontal discontinuity plane, would not define a kinematically feasible block. Figure 7.3c shows a lower-hemisphere projection of the great circles of the three

discontinuity planes involved. These great circles intersect each other to close off a curved triangular shape, here referred to as a spherical triangle, and indicated by the hatching on the projection in Figure 7.3c. In this figure the great circle of a plane from set 1 forms the southeastern boundary of the spherical triangle, set 2 forms the northern boundary and set 3 the southwestern boundary. In other words, the relative locations of the three great circles on the spherical triangle are the same as the relative physical locations of their respective planes when they delimit a kinematically feasible tetrahedral block at the given face. This important property of a spherical triangle, here referred to as kinematic congruence, occurs when the following two kinematic conditions of projection are met:

(a) The plane of projection must be parallel to the face that is being studied.
(b) The hemisphere of projection must be convex towards the free-air side of the face.

These conditions are always satisfied, for a horizontal overhanging face, by an ordinary lower-hemisphere projection, as shown in Figures 7.3a and 7.3c. This can be appreciated by imagining the tetrahedral block, illustrated in Figure 7.3a, to be placed at its correct orientation on top of the projection in Figure 7.3c. The plane of projection would then represent the rock face; the block would exist on the rock mass side of the face and the hemisphere of projection would exist on the free air side. The point of observation would be from within the rock mass, looking out into free air along the normal to the face.

If a projection can be constructed so that the kinematic conditions of projection are satisfied for a given face then any spherical triangle on this projection, formed by three non-parallel planes of any orientations, will be kinematically congruent with a feasible tetrahedral block at the face. For example, if there were five discontinuity sets they could, by combining in different ways, define ten different tetrahedral blocks such as: rock face, set 1, set 2 plus set 3; or rock face, set 1, set 2 plus set 4; etc. In general, if there are n discontinuity sets, the number of different tetrahedral blocks is given by

$$t = n!/6((n-3)!)$$

Figure 7.4 shows how the great circles of five non-parallel planes intersect to give ten different spherical triangles. In general, n non-parallel planes always intersect to give t spherical triangles, each of which is associated with a different tetrahedral block. If the projection statisfies the two kinematic conditions of projection, listed above, for a given face, then each spherical triangle will be kinematically congruent with its respective tetrahedral block at the face. Since kinematic congruence greatly facilitates the visualisation of the geometry of kinematically feasible tetrahedral blocks, it is desirable to be able to satisfy these two conditions for any inclined overhanging or non-overhanging face that is being analysed. This ensures that the geometries of kinematically feasible tetrahedral blocks are directly related to the geometries of their spherical triangles on the projection.

7.3 Construction of inclined hemisphere projections

7.3.1 Construction methods

The process of satisfying the two conditions of projection for a non-horizontal face, in order to generate spherical triangles that are kinematically congruent with the given face, leads to the concept of inclined hemisphere projection (Priest 1980). This involves rotating, or inclining, the hemisphere of projection so that (1) the plane of projection is parallel to the face, and (2) the hemisphere of projection is convex towards the free air side of the face. It may be helpful at this stage to imagine the hemisphere, illustrated in Figure 2.8, being physically inclined and then placed like a 'bubble' on the rock face as shown in Figure 7.5. It has already been shown that, if the face is horizontal and

overhanging, no inclination is required. If the face were overhanging but dipped at an an angle of 50°, then 50° of inclination would be required. If the face were vertical, then 90° of inclination would be required. If the face were horizontal and non-overhanging then 180° of inclination would be required. If the face were non-overhanging but dipped at angle of, say 60°, then 120° of inclination would be required (i.e. 180 − 60), as shown in Figure 7.5. In general, if the free face has an angle of dip β_f, then the required angle of inclination is given by ϱ_f as follows

$$\begin{aligned} \varrho_f &= \beta_f && \text{for an overhanging face} \\ \varrho_f &= 180 - \beta_f && \text{for a non-overhanging face} \end{aligned} \tag{7.1}$$

During this inclination, the absolute orientations of the discontinuity planes, the rock face and other fixed features do not change. Consequently the great circles and normals representing the orientations of such features will track across the projection as the hemisphere is inclined. This effect is rather similar to the apparent movement of the stars as the Earth rotates. In practice, it is not necessary actually to incline the hemisphere of projection physically as long as the apparent rotations of all the various fixed features are correctly represented.

The aim of inclining the hemisphere of projection is to ensure that the plane of projection becomes parallel to the rock face. This means that the normal to the rock face, N_f, must be rotated until it plots at the centre of the projection, as illustrated in Figure 7.5. This can only be achieved

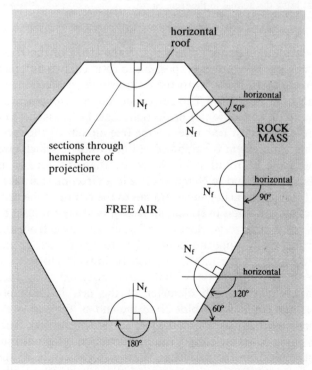

Figure 7.5 Inclining the hemisphere to make the plane of projection parallel to the rock face.

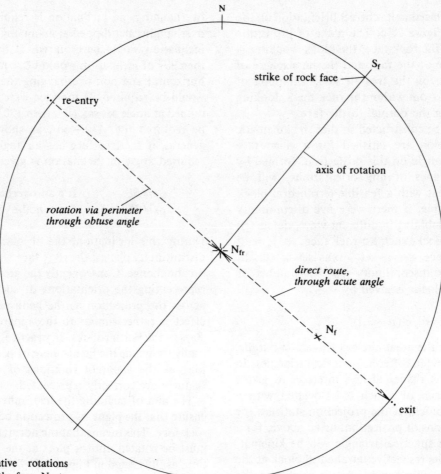

Figure 7.6 Two alternative rotations that bring the normal to the face, N_f, to the centre of the projection.

by a rotation about an axis that is the strike of the given rock face. It is, however, possible to rotate in two different directions to bring N_f to the centre of the projection, as shown in Figure 7.6 The correct direction is governed by the second condition of projection: that the hemisphere of projection must be convex to the free air side of the face. This requirement is embodied in Equations 7.1 which give the angle of rotation ϱ_f. At an overhanging face ϱ_f is always acute and so N_f must rotate in a direction that takes it through the acute angle straight to the centre of the projection. At a non-overhanging face ϱ_f is always obtuse, so N_f must first rotate to the perimeter and then from the diametrically opposite point move to the centre of the projection. If the face is vertical, N_f initially plots at the perimeter. In this case, with the strike direction of the face on the north–south diameter of the net, it is simply necessary initially to plot N_f at the end of the east–west diameter that places it on the free air side of the rock face. If this is done, the correct rotation direction is the one that takes N_f from the perimeter directly to the centre of the projection. Whatever the orientation of the face, the crucial feature about this rotation is that all other data points on the projection must be rotated by the same

amount, ϱ_f, as N_f, about the same axis and in the same direction in order to maintain their correct relative orientations. During this process it is much easier to rotate single data points, such as the normals to planes, rather than attempting to rotate complete great circles.

7.3.2 Summary and examples
The process of constructing an inclined hemisphere projection can now be summarised as follows.

(1) The following data points are plotted and clearly labelled on an ordinary lower-hemisphere projection: The normals N_1, N_2, N_3, etc., and also the lines of maximum dip D_1, D_2, D_3, etc., of the various discontinuity planes and additional free faces are plotted in the usual way. Their great circles are not, however, plotted at this stage. The strike direction S_f, the normal N_f and the line of maximum dip D_f of the rock face are also plotted. Finally the normal to the horizontal, N_h, is plotted at the centre of the projection; this, of course, gives the vertical direction.

(2) The required angle of rotation, ϱ_f, for a face dipping at an angle β_f is found from Equations 7.1, taking

care to note the distinction between an overhanging and a non-overhanging face.

(3) The strike direction of the face, S_f, is placed on the north–south diameter of the net. If the angle ϱ_f is acute (i.e. the face is overhanging) then the direction of rotation is such that N_f moves through the angle ϱ_f directly to the centre of the projection along the east–west diameter. If ϱ_f is obtuse (i.e. the face is non-overhanging) then the required rotation must be in a direction that first takes N_f to the perimeter, to re-enter at a diametrically opposite point and continue its rotation to the centre of the projection. If the face is vertical, N_f is initially plotted on the free air side of the face and then rotated directly to the centre of the projection.

(4) All other data points are then rotated along small circles, by the same amount, ϱ_f, as N_f, about the same axis and in the same direction. Any point that leaves the perimeter of the projection continues its rotation after re-entering at a diametrically opposite point in the usual way. The rotated line of maximum dip of the rock face, which always ends up on the perimeter of the projection, is plotted at the point where it first intersects this perimeter and is not transferred across the diameter. It may be helpful to add a subscript 'r' to the label for each rotated point to differentiate it from the original point.

(5) The great circles of the various discontinuity planes, and also the horizontal plane, are plotted from their respective normals by applying the same basic principles as those used when plotting great circles and their normals on an ordinary lower-hemisphere projection (Section 3.3). Although the rotated line of maximum dip of a given discontinuity plane always plots at some point along its respective great circle, only in very special circumstances does it plot at the usual midpoint.

The great circle of the horizontal plane divides the projection into two zones: one above and one below the horizontal. The rotated line of maximum dip of the rock face, D_{fr}, always plots on the perimeter of the projection, at the bottom edge of the zone that is below the horizontal. It is usually helpful, therefore, to place the point D_{fr} at the southern azimuth of the net, in order to facilitate interpretation.

All spherical triangles plotted on an inclined hemisphere projection, constructed by the above method, are kinematically congruent with blocks at the given rock face. This greatly facilitates the analysis of the associated tetrahedral blocks at the face. Before considering the interpretation of an inclined hemisphere projection, it may be helpful to work through the following examples of construction.

Example 7.1 (Fig. 7.7) A planar overhanging rock face of dip direction/dip amount 120/50 is intersected by five persistent, planar discontinuity sets with the following orientations:

Set	Dip direction (deg)	Dip amount (deg)
1	185	54
2	117	70
3	150	81
4	325	32
5	048	64

Construct the inclined hemisphere projection for this face.

The normals $N_1, N_2, \ldots, N_5$ and also the lines of maximum dip $D_1, D_2, \ldots, D_5$ of the five discontinuity orientations are plotted on an ordinary lower-hemisphere projection in the usual way, as shown in Figure 7.7. The strike direction, normal and line of maximum dip of the rock face are also plotted and labelled S_f, N_f and D_f respectively. The centre of the projection, which initially represents the normal to the horizontal, is labelled N_h. No great circles are plotted at this stage. In this example the rock face is overhanging and dips at an angle of 50°; the required angle of rotation, ϱ_f, is therefore 50°. With the axis of rotation, S_f, on the north–south diameter of the net, the direction of rotation is such that N_f moves directly to the centre of the projection through the angle 50°. All the other data points are then rotated along small circles by the same amount, about the same axis and in the same direction. These rotated points are labelled 'r' to avoid confusion with the original points. Finally the great circles of the five discontinuity planes, and also the horizontal plane, are plotted from their respective rotated normals. This is achieved by first placing the rotated normal on the east–west diameter of the net and then counting 90° from the normal, along this diameter and through the centre of the net. The great circle that lies 90° from the normal is traced off in the usual way and labelled as shown in Figure 7.7. This labelling is particularly important when a large number of discontinuities are being plotted. It may also be helpful to differentiate between normals and lines of maximum dip, by representing each of the former as a dot and the latter by a small cross, as shown in Figure 7.7.

It is worth reiterating that, although the rotated lines of maximum dip always plot on their respective great circles, they do not generally occur at the usual midpoint. This requirement that a given great circle should contain its line of maximum dip provides a valuable check on the construction since the two are plotted independently. If this independent check is not required, the lines of maximum dip can be omitted from the initial lower-hemisphere plot,

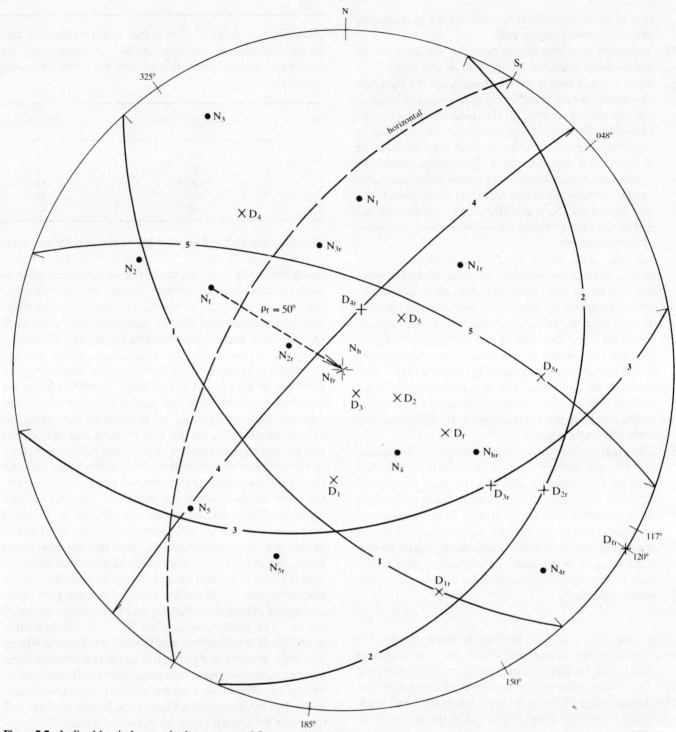

Figure 7.7 Inclined hemisphere projection constructed for an overhanging face of dip direction/dip amount 120/50 (Examples 7.1 and 7.3).

thereby almost halving the number of points that require rotation. This is possible because the rotated line of maximum dip, D_{ir}, of the ith plane on an inclined hemisphere projection can always be plotted by reference to the rotated normal, N_{ir}, to this plane and the rotated normal to the horizontal, N_{hr}. Since N_{hr} represents the vertical direction, any great circle that passes through N_{hr} must represent a vertical plane. Moreover, any great circle

that contains both N_{hr} and N_{ir} must represent a vertical plane that also contains D_{ir}. This rotated line of maximum dip therefore plots on its associated great circle 90° from N_{ir} measured in the usual way along the great circle containing N_{hr} and N_{ir}. The rotated line of maximum dip for a given plane is of great value when interpreting block behaviour under simple gravitational loading.

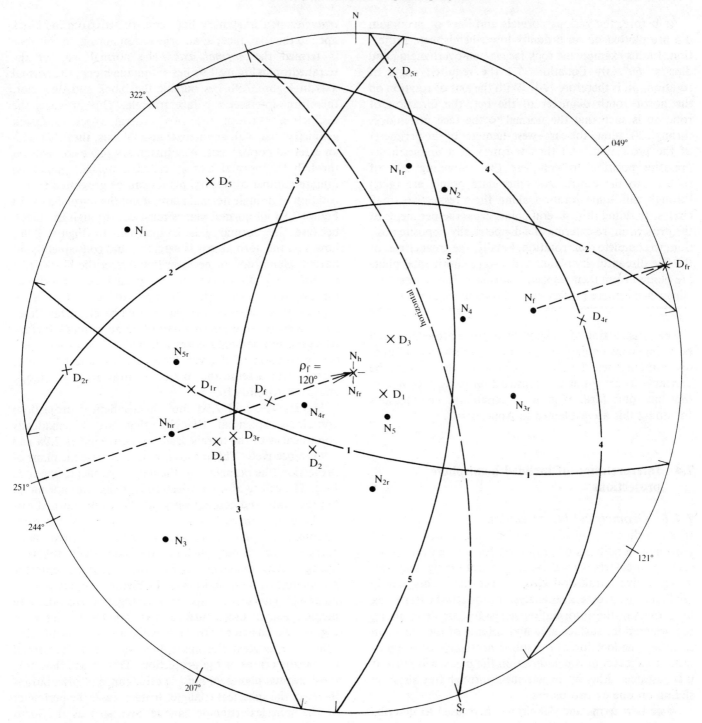

Figure 7.8 Inclined hemisphere projection constructed for a non-overhanging face of dip direction/dip amount 251/60 (Examples 7.2 and 7.4).

Example 7.2 (Fig. 7.8) A planar non-overhanging rock face of dip direction/dip amount 251/60 is intersected by five sets of persistent, planar discontinuities with the following orientations:

Set	Dip direction (deg)	Dip amount (deg)
1	121	77
2	207	62
3	049	73
4	244	41
5	322	19

Construct the inclined hemisphere projection for this face.

As before, the various normals and lines of maximum dip are plotted on an ordinary lower-hemisphere projection. In this example the rock face is non-overhanging and dips at 60°. By Equations 7.1 the required angle of rotation, ϱ_f, is therefore 120°. With the axis of rotation on the north–south diameter of the net, the direction of rotation is such that the normal to the face first moves through 30° along the east–west diameter to the perimeter of the projection, and then re-enters at a diametrically opposite position to complete the remaining 90° of rotation to the centre. All other data points are taken through this same rotation along their respective small circles. In doing this, several points cross the perimeter of the projection, re-entering at a diametrically opposite position, to complete their rotation. Finally, the great circles of the five discontinuity planes and also the horizontal plane are plotted from their respective normals. The resulting inclined hemisphere projection is shown in Figure 7.8.

The construction of inclined hemisphere projections can be a time-consuming process if there are several different discontinuity sets involved. In view of this it may be desirable to carry out the construction using a computer that has some form of graphics capability. The methods for doing this are explained in Appendix C.

7.4 Interpretation of inclined hemisphere projections

7.4.1 Geometrical interpretation

If an inclined hemisphere projection satisfies the two kinematic conditions of projection for a given face, then each spherical triangle will be kinematically congruent with its respective tetrahedral block at the face. This greatly facilitates the geometrical analysis of the tetrahedral block by providing the information necessary for determining the orientation, surface area and volume of the block. In addition, the location of the spherical triangle on the projection indicates in which direction the block will move if it is unstable, either by displacement through free air or by sliding on one or two planes.

Some new terms and definitions, here used to describe the geometry of tetrahedral blocks and their associated spherical triangles, are explained below. Figures 7.9a and 7.9b show two types of kinematically feasible tetrahedral block geometries that can be formed by three discontinuity planes and a planar free face. In each case the three discontinuity planes intersect in pairs to form three *block corners*, labelled I_{12}, I_{23}, etc. These three corners intersect at a point, here termed the *block apex*. The three discontinuities intersect the rock face to delimit the *face triangle*. The remaining three sides of the tetrahedron, formed by the three discontinuity planes, are here termed *block surface*

triangles. An imaginary line, constructed from the block apex to the rock face, at an orientation normal to this face is termed the *normal axis*. The normal axis of the tetrahedron in Figure 7.9a lies within the block; the normal axis in Figure 7.9b lies outside the block and does not, therefore, intersect the face triangle. This provides the distinction between the two general types of block geometry: one with an internal normal axis, the other with an external normal axis. Any imaginary plane constructed through the normal axis is called a *normal plane*; an infinite number of normal planes can be generated by the rotation of a single normal plane about the normal axis. In Figure 7.9a all normal planes must cut through the block because the normal axis is internal. In Figure 7.9b, however, the normal axis is external, and consequently all normal planes do not necessarily intersect the block. If a normal plane does intersect any given block, it will cut through two block surface triangles to define two *block surface lines*. Block corners are special block surface lines since they are common to a pair of adjacent block surface triangles. For some purposes it is convenient to represent the orientation of a given block surface line by a unit vector, with a sense that directs it away from the block apex, out towards free air.

Figures 7.9c and 7.9d show hemispherical projections containing spherical triangles that are kinematically congruent with the tetrahedral blocks in Figures 7.9a and 7.9b respectively. This means that in each case the plane of projection (the perimeter of the net) is parallel to the rock face. The centre of the projection is, therefore, normal to the rock face and consequently parallel to the normal axis of the block. In each case the great circles of the three discontinuity planes intersect to give the three block corners and thereby delimit the congruent spherical triangle. Any diameter of the projection represents the great circle of a normal plane. In Figure 7.9c any normal plane will intersect the spherical triangle at two points to define a pair of block surface lines. The block relating to Figure 7.9d has an external normal axis; consequently, the spherical triangle in this figure does not enclose the normal axis at the centre of the projection. This means that only those normal planes within a specific range of orientations intersect the spherical triangle. In each case, the perimeter of the spherical triangle can be envisaged as the locus generated by an infinite number of block surface lines radiating from the block apex towards the rock face. It is important to appreciate that it is always possible to find a line that radiates from the block apex and lies in a given discontinuity plane, but that is not a block surface line for the given block. Such a line, shown in Figure 7.9c, does not lie on the congruent spherical triangle and must, therefore, have an orientation that places it outside the physical surface of the given block. Any block that is deduced to have a sliding mechanism of failure must, if unstable, slide along a block surface line.

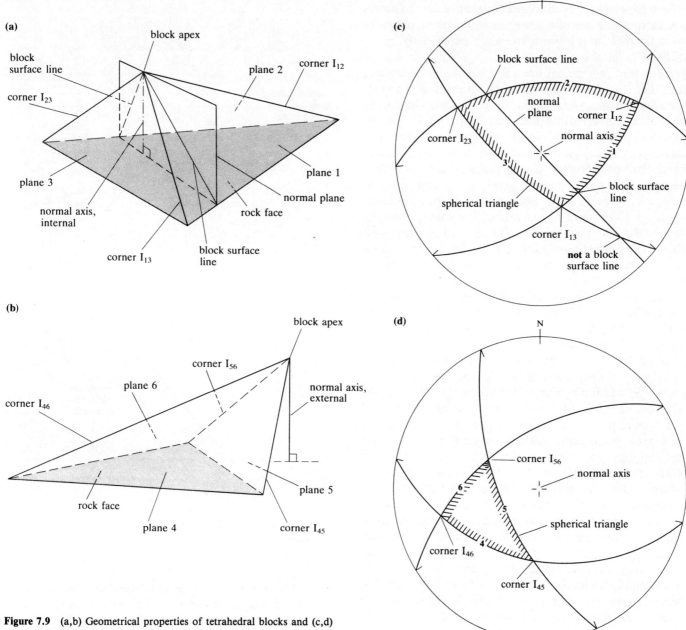

Figure 7.9 (a,b) Geometrical properties of tetrahedral blocks and (c,d) their respective kinematically congruent spherical triangles.

Figures 7.7 and 7.8 each contain ten different spherical triangles; some of these enclose the centre of the projection and therefore have an internal normal axis, others do not enclose the centre and therefore have an external normal axis. When the rotated line of maximum dip of the rock face, D_{fr}, is placed at the southern azimuth of the net, the strike of the rock face will lie on the east–west diameter of the net. It may be helpful, when the projection is in this position, to imagine oneself sitting inside the rock mass so that the inclined hemisphere projection represents the 'view' looking out towards free air along the normal to the rock face. The north, south, east and west points of the net

should now be interpreted as: up, down, right and left respectively in the plane of the inclined face. The great circle of the rotated horizontal plane intersects the great circle of each plane on the projection to define, in each case, the strike of the plane. Any point that plots on the same side of the horizontal plane as D_{fr} plots below the horizontal; any point that plots on the opposite side from D_{fr} plots above the horizontal.

When dealing with purely geometrical features it is not necessary to consider the sense of the associated line. For simplicity, therefore, on an ordinary lower-hemisphere projection, all such lines have been assumed to have a downward sense. In a similar way, on an inclined hemisphere projection, it is convenient to assume that all purely geometrical lines are of a sense that directs them outwards from the rock mass towards free air. Consequently, on an inclined hemisphere projection, if a point representing some purely geometrical line plots below the horizontal, then the line is interpreted to be directed downwards towards free air. A geometrical point that plots above the horizontal represents a line that is directed upwards towards free air. The angle of plunge of the line represented by any given point can be found on an inclined hemisphere projection by placing the point and the rotated vertical, N_{hr}, on a common great circle. The angle of plunge is the acute angle measured along this great circle from the given point to the rotated horizontal plane. In some cases this may be the external angle on the great circle. The steepest downward-directed line on a projection constructed for an overhanging face is given by the rotated vertical, N_{hr}. The steepest downward-directed line on a projection for a non-overhanging face is given by the rotated line of maximum dip, D_{fr}, of the face. In either case, this steepest line can be interpreted as the 'bottom point' of the projection.

When one or more additional planar free faces occur in the vicinity of the main rock face, it is quite permissible to treat each additional planar face in exactly the same way as a discontinuity plane when constructing the inclined hemisphere projection for the main face. Any additional free face can, under certain circumstances, intersect discontinuity planes and/or other free faces, to define a kinematically feasible tetrahedral block, the geometry of which is directly related to the associated kinematically congruent spherical triangle on the projection, in the usual way. It is important to bear in mind, however, that rock exists on only one side of any given free face. Consequently, if a kinematically congruent spherical triangle, comprising an additional free face, constructs the associated block on the free air side of that face, then that block cannot exist. If one or more additional free faces are to be involved in delimiting a valid tetrahedral block, then the associated kinematically congruent spherical triangle must exist on the rock mass side of each face. This means that, in order to delimit a valid block, an overhanging additional free face can only participate in spherical triangles that lie above it on the projection; a non-overhanging free face can only participate in spherical triangles that lie below it. These restrictions only apply when the additional free face actually forms part of a given spherical triangle; those triangles involving three discontinuity planes are interpreted in the usual way. In some situations the actual location(s) of the additional free face(s) may be known. In this case only those free faces that exist on the rock mass side of the main face need be included in the analysis. Those free faces on the free air side of the main face create re-entrant corners that cannot

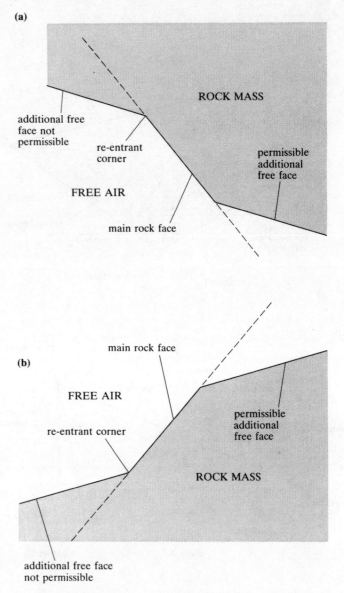

Figure 7.10 Permissible locations of additional free faces (a) at an overhanging main face and (b) at a non-overhanging main face.

form tetrahedral blocks. This is illustrated in Figure 7.10. The most common situation involving an additional free face is where a non-overhanging rock slope has a 'top' formed by a non-overhanging free face, which often has a relatively small angle of dip.

7.4.2 Interpretation of block behaviour under general conditions of loading

The stability, and if it is unstable also the failure mechanism, of a given block depends upon the orientation, magnitude and sense of the resultant force vector **r** that acts upon the block. The methods for determining **r**, which must include a calculation of the block weight and also an analysis of the external forces, are explained in detail in the next chapter. Until then, the orientation, magnitude and sense of this resultant force are assumed to be known.

When force vectors are plotted on a lower-hemisphere projection, it is vitally important to record also the sense of each force, as discussed in the previous chapter. Depending on its orientation and its sense, a given resultant force **r** may be directed either outwards towards free air or inwards towards the rock mass. In order to assess this, it is first necessary to represent the orientation of the resultant force on the appropriate inclined hemisphere projection, by taking the point **r** through the rotation ϱ_f in the usual way, to give the rotated resultant force $\mathbf{r_r}$. The assessment, which is based upon the sense of **r** and the position of $\mathbf{r_r}$ on the inclined hemisphere projection, is summarised in Table 7.1.

When analysing the way in which a given block will behave it is assumed that the block will tend to move in the direction of the resultant force vector, $\mathbf{r_r}$, unless prevented from doing so by the rock mass adjacent to the discontinuity planes that delimit the block. Such a constraint occurs if one, or more, of these discontinuity planes is orientated so that it, or they, is maintained in a state of compression by $\mathbf{r_r}$. In this case the block can only fail by sliding on one, or two, compressive plane(s) along the block surface line associated with the largest value of shear stress in this, or these, plane(s). This potential sliding direction is given by the block surface line that makes the smallest acute solid angle with $\mathbf{r_r}$. If each block surface line is regarded as a unit vector radiating from the block apex out towards free air, this acute angle must be measured between its positive end and the positive end of $\mathbf{r_r}$. Consequently, if $\mathbf{r_r}$ is directed outwards towards free air this acute angle must be measured internally on the inclined hemisphere projection. However, if $\mathbf{r_r}$ is directed inwards towards the rock mass it is necessary to measure this acute angle externally on the projection. In this latter case it is more convenient to determine the sliding direction by locating the block surface line that makes the largest obtuse angle with $\mathbf{r_r}$ when measured internally on the projection. This angle is therefore, in this latter case, measured from the negative end of the vector $\mathbf{r_r}$. This always gives the same result as that obtained by taking the smallest acute external angle but is somewhat easier to measure and to visualise. If it is found that the smallest solid angle between a block surface line and $\mathbf{r_r}$ is greater than $90°$, then the associated block cannot become unstable because the resultant force, whatever its magnitude, generates shear components that tend to drive the block into the rock mass. These ideas are explained in more detail, and in more formal terms, below.

The perimeter of any kinematically congruent spherical triangle gives the locus of block surface lines for the associated block. The relation between the geometry of the block and the orientation of the resultant force that acts upon it is expressed in terms of the angle θ measured from

Table 7.1 Interpretation of the sense of a force on an inclined hemisphere projection.

Sense of force **r**	Position of $\mathbf{r_r}$ on the inclined hemisphere projection	
	Plots above the horizontal plane	Plots below the horizontal plane
upward sense	force is directed outwards towards free air	force is directed inwards towards the rock mass
downward sense	force is directed inwards towards the rock mass	force is directed outwards towards free air

$\mathbf{r_r}$ to the point, L, which represents a block surface line on the perimeter of the associated spherical triangle. This angle θ is counted *internally* along the great circle containing $\mathbf{r_r}$ and L and will, therefore, lie in the range $0 < \theta < 180°$. On a given spherical triangle there will always be a single point, L_{min}, representing the block surface line that makes the minimum possible angle, θ_{min}, with $\mathbf{r_r}$. There will also be another single point, L_{max}, representing the block surface line that makes the maximum possible angle, θ_{max}, with $\mathbf{r_r}$. Either of these points, L_{min} or L_{max}, may represent a line that lies in a single discontinuity plane or alternatively at a block corner, depending upon the orientation of $\mathbf{r_r}$ and the geometry of the block. There can, in fact, only ever be up to six possible candidates for L_{min} and L_{max} on a given spherical triangle. The first three candidates lie on each of the three planes involved, at the point where each plane is intersected by the great circle that contains both $\mathbf{r_r}$ and the rotated normal to the plane. However, if the point defined in this way does not lie on the spherical triangle it must be eliminated since it does not represent a block surface line. The remaining three possible candidates are the corners of the spherical triangle, which represent the three block corners. These measurements are illustrated in Figure 7.11, which is the inclined hemisphere projection previously presented in Figure 7.7 but, in this case, only containing planes 1, 2 and 3 and their rotated normals. It is assumed that the resultant vector **r** acting on the block has a dip direction/dip amount 333/28 and a downward sense. The inclined hemisphere representation of this vector, labelled $\mathbf{r_r}$, was obtained by rotation in the usual way. The angles θ measured from $\mathbf{r_r}$ to the extreme points on planes 1, 2 and 3 are $63°$, $56°$ and $70°$ respectively. The extreme points on planes 1 and 2 do not, however, lie on the spherical triangle and so are ignored. The angles θ measured from $\mathbf{r_r}$ to the corners of the spherical triangle are $96°$ for the intersection between planes 1 and 2, $72°$ for 2 and 3, and $79°$ for 1 and 3. Hence θ_{min} is $70°$ and L_{min} lies on plane 3; θ_{max} is $96°$ and L_{max} is the corner formed by the intersection between planes 1 and 2.

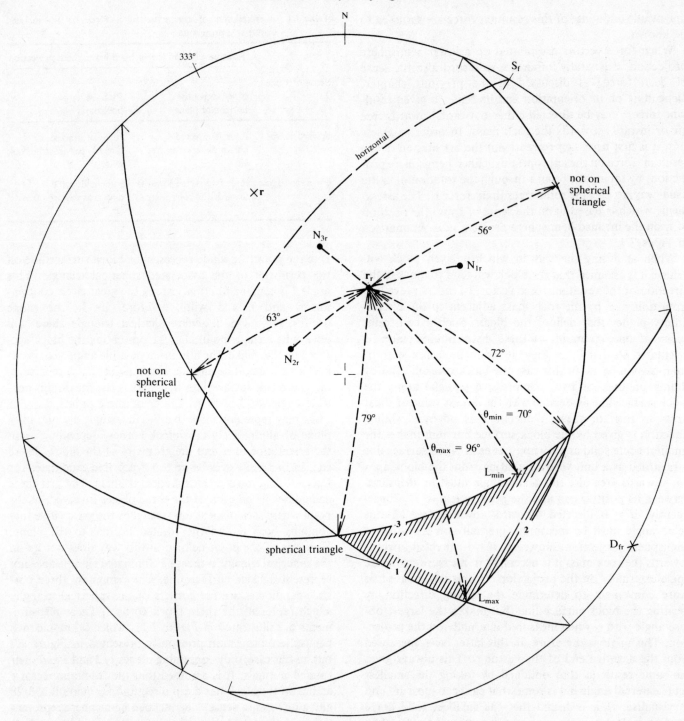

Figure 7.11 Determination of the extreme points L_{min} and L_{max} on a spherical triangle.

The values of θ_{min} and θ_{max}, and also the sense and orientation of $\mathbf{r_r}$, are important indicators of how the associated tetrahedral block will behave. The various possible combinations of these values give rise to five different categories of block behaviour as explained below, summarised in Table 7.2 and also illustrated in Figure 7.12. For clarity in this figure, the resultant vector has been drawn so that it acts through the apex of each block. In general, however, this vector is assumed to act through the centre of mass of a given block. In cases where $\mathbf{r_r}$ is directed inwards towards the rock mass, the internal angle θ_{max} must be measured from its negative end.

It $\mathbf{r_r}$ is directed outwards towards free air and also plots outside the spherical triangle, then the behaviour of the associated block depends only upon the value of θ_{min}: if $\theta_{min} \geq 90°$ then the associated block cannot move

Table 7.2 Behaviour of kinematically feasible tetrahedral blocks subject to a general resultant force vector **r**.

	r_r is directed outwards towards free air		**r_r is directed inwards towards the rock mass**	
	$\theta_{min} \geqslant 90°$	$\theta_{min} < 90°$	$\theta_{max} \leqslant 90°$	$\theta_{max} > 90°$
r_r plots outside the spherical triangle	Ia associated block cannot move	IIa associated block if unstable, slides outwards along L_{min} [a]	Ib associated block canot move	IIb associated b lock, if unstable slides outwards along L_{max} [b]
r_r plots inside the spherical triangle	III associated block, if unstable, moves in the direction of r_r			

[a] L_{min} = block surface line that makes the smallest acute angle, θ_{min}, with **r_r**.
[b] L_{max} = block surface line that makes the largest obtuse angle, θ_{max}, with **r_r**.

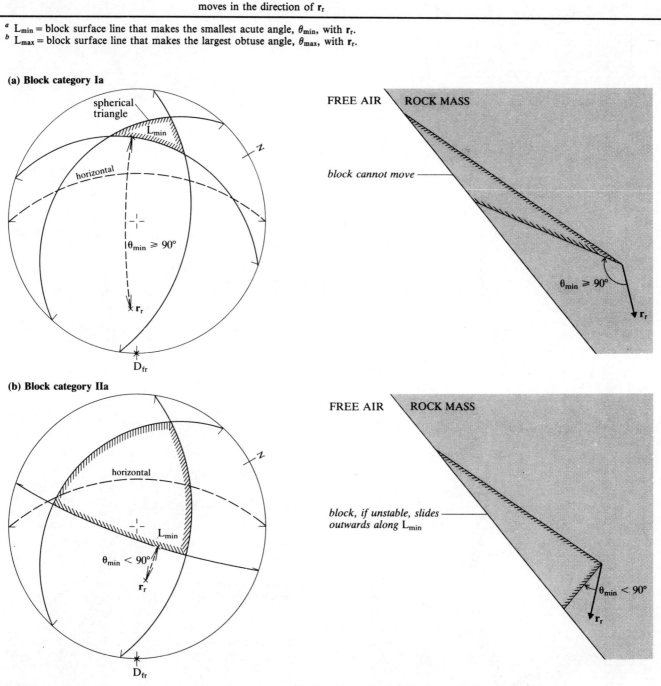

(a) Block category Ia

(b) Block category IIa

Figure 7.12 Behaviour of kinematically feasible tetrahedral blocks subjected to a general resultant force vector **r_r**.

(c) Block category Ib

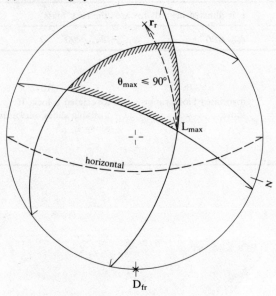

(d) Block category IIb

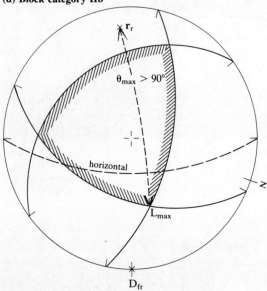

(e) Block category III

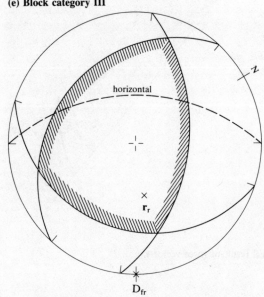

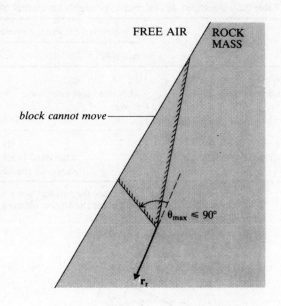

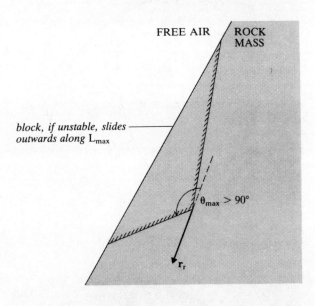

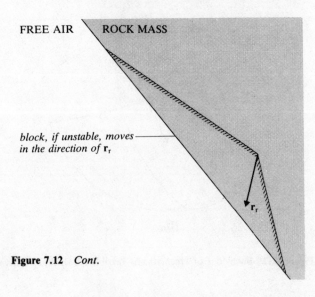

Figure 7.12 *Cont.*

(category Ia, Fig. 7.12a); if $\theta_{min} < 90°$ then the associated block, if unstable, will slide outwards towards free air along the block surface line represented by the point L_{min} (category IIa, Fig. 7.12b). If $\mathbf{r}_r$ is directed inwards towards the rock mass, then the behaviour of the associated block depends only upon the value of θ_{max} irrespective of whether $\mathbf{r}_r$ plots outside or within the spherical triangle: if $\theta_{max} \leqslant 90°$ then the associated block cannot move (category Ib, Fig. 7.12c); if $\theta_{max} > 90°$ then the associated block, if unstable, will slide outwards towards free air along the block surface line represented by L_{max} (category IIb, Fig. 7.12d). If $\mathbf{r}_r$ is directed outwards towards free air and also plots within the spherical triangle then the associated block, if unstable, will move through free air in the direction of $\mathbf{r}_r$ (category III, Fig. 7.12e).

Blocks in category I cannot move because the resultant force vector generates shear components that tend to drive the block into the rock mass. Blocks in category II undergo sliding, if unstable, because the resultant force vector generates shear components that tend to drive the block out towards free air by sliding along one, or two, planes that are maintained in a state of compression. If the appropriate extreme point, L_{min} or L_{max}, lies on a single plane then the block, if unstable, will slide on that single plane. If the extreme point represents a block corner then the block, if unstable, will slide along the line of intersection of the two planes that form the corner. The true trend and plunge of the sliding direction can be found by reversing the rotation, ϱ_f, for the point, or alternatively by replotting the planes involved on an ordinary lower-hemisphere projection. Blocks in category IIa are more likely to be unstable if θ_{min} is small; those in category IIb are more likely to be unstable if θ_{max} is large. Blocks in category III are effectively 'pulled' from the rock mass since the resultant force vector induces separation across each discontinuity plane.

If the block under analysis is formed by a valid combination of discontinuity planes and one or more additional free faces, it is necessary to consider the possibility that the block may fail by displacing from one of the additional free faces. If a given block has been classified as category I at the main face, this possibility can be investigated by constructing an inclined hemisphere projection for each additional free face in turn. When interpreting spherical triangles involving additional free faces, it is important to recognise that a free face can never form a sliding plane, either on its own or in combination with a discontinuity plane since sliding requires a rock-to-rock interface. In practice, this complication very rarely arises when analysing valid tetrahedral blocks since in most cases the additional free face is non-overhanging and forms the upper surface of the block.

Returning to the illustration in Figure 7.11, the resultant vector acting on the block has a downward sense and, since $\mathbf{r}_r$ plots below the horizontal it must be directed outwards

towards free air (Table 7.1). Since $\mathbf{r}_r$ plots outside the spherical triangle in Figure 7.11 and $\theta_{min} < 90°$, the associated block, if unstable, will slide outwards along L_{min}, which in this case lies on plane 3. The true trend and plunge of the block surface line, L_{min}, found by reversing the rotation ϱ_f for this point, are 116/79.

The principles set out in this section, and summarised in Table 7.2 and Figure 7.12, are of vital importance when predicting failure mechanisms and analysing the stability of tetrahedral blocks. Further generalised analysis of resultant force vectors and their influence on the behaviour of tetrahedral blocks will, however, be postponed until the next chapter, when the methods for determining these resultant vectors will be explained. In the meantime, it is worth while considering the simple, but relatively common, case where a given block is subject only to simple gravitational loading.

7.4.3 Interpretation of block behaviour under simple gravitational loading

In dry rock masses, and where there are no external forces such as rock bolt loads, blocks are often subject only to simple gravitational loading. In such cases the resultant force vector $\mathbf{r}$ on the block acts in a vertical direction with a downward sense. The orientation of $\mathbf{r}_r$ on the inclined hemisphere projection is therefore given by the rotated vertical, N_{hr}. At any overhanging face, $\mathbf{r}_r$ plots below the horizontal and is therefore directed outwards towards free air; at any non-overhanging face, $\mathbf{r}_r$ plots above the horizontal and is therefore directed inwards towards the rock mass (Table 7.1). Since, during construction, the line of maximum dip of the face is not transferred across the diameter of the projection, a vertical face must be interpreted as if it were overhanging. On any inclined hemisphere projection, the horizontal plane gives the locus of points that make an angle of 90° with N_{hr}. It is now possible, therefore, to rewrite the generalised interpretation, set out in Table 7.2, for the specific case of blocks that are subject only to simple gravitational loading. The resulting interpretation, which is given in Table 7.3 and illustrated in Figure 7.13, is equivalent in all respects to the generalised interpretation described in the previous section and summarised in Table 7.2 and Figure 7.12. As before, there can only ever be up to six possible candidates for L_{min} and L_{max} on a given spherical triangle. In this case, however, the first three candidates are given by the rotated lines of maximum dip, D_{ir}, of the three planes involved since these lines must be coplanar with the associated normal, N_{ir}, and the vertical resultant force. Again, if one of these points does not lie on the spherical triangle, it must be eliminated since it does not represent a block surface line. As before, the remaining three possible candidates are the corners of the spherical triangle, which represent the three block corners. In most cases, therefore, it is relatively easy to identify L_{min} and L_{max} simply by inspecting the lines

Table 7.3 Behaviour of kinematically feasible tetrahedral blocks subject only to simple gravitational loading.

	Overhanging (or vertical) rock face, $\mathbf{r}_r$ directed outwards towards free air		Non-overhanging rock face, $\mathbf{r}_r$ directed inwards towards the rock mass	
	Spherical triangle plots entirely above the horizontal plane	Part of spherical triangle plots below the horizontal plane	Spherical triangle plots entirely above the horizontal plane	Part of spherical triangle plots below the horizontal plane
N_{hr} plots outside the spherical triangle	Ia associated block directed upwards, cannot move	IIa associated block, if unstable, slides outwards along L_{min} [a]	Ib associated block directed upwards, cannot move	IIb associated block, if unstable, slides outwards along L_{max} [b]
N_{hr} plots inside the spherical triangle	III associated block, if unstable, falls vertically			

[a] L_{min} = block surface line that makes the smallest acute angle, θ_{min}, with N_{hr}.
[b] L_{max} = block surface line that makes the largest obtuse angle, θ_{max}, with N_{hr}.

(a) Block category Ia

(b) Block category IIa

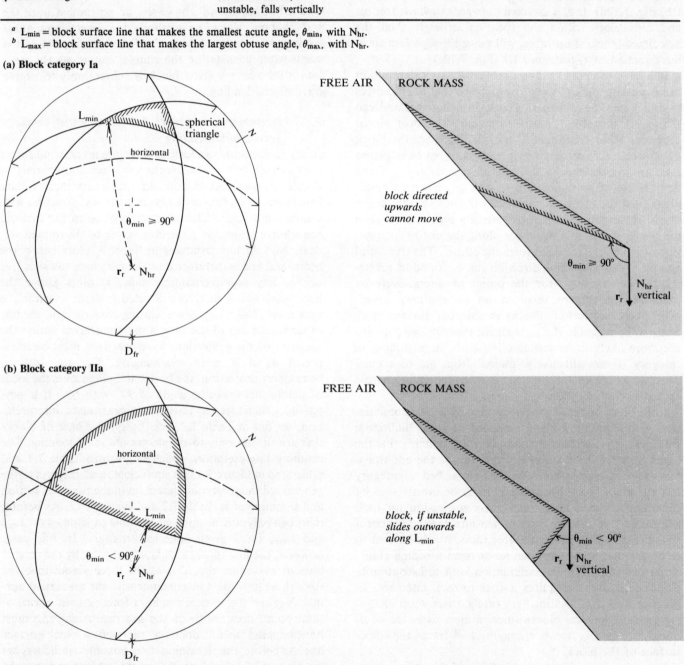

Figure 7.13 Behaviour of kinematically feasible tetrahedral blocks subjected only to simple gravitational loading.

(c) Block category Ib

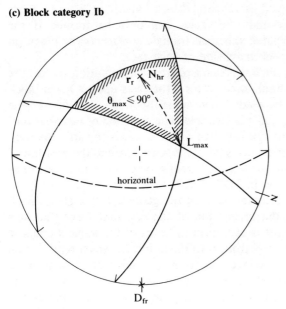

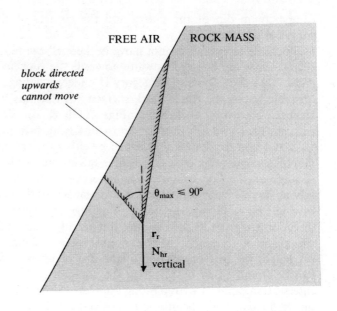

block directed upwards cannot move

$\theta_{max} \leqslant 90°$

$\mathbf{r}_r$
N_{hr}
vertical

(d) Block category IIb

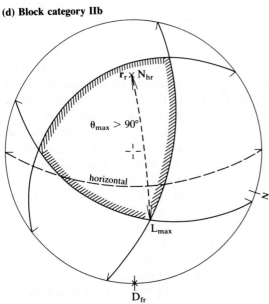

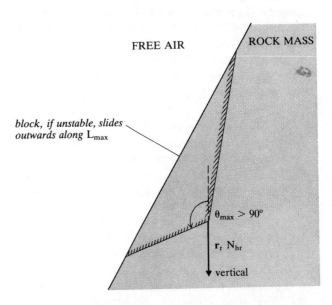

block, if unstable, slides outwards along L_{max}

$\theta_{max} > 90°$

$\mathbf{r}_r\ N_{hr}$
vertical

(e) Block category III

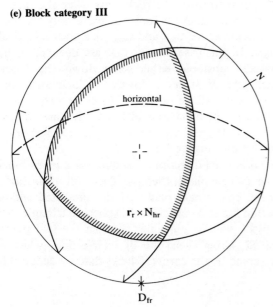

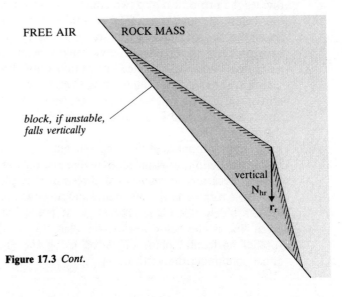

block, if unstable, falls vertically

vertical
N_{hr}
$\mathbf{r}_r$

Figure 17.3 *Cont.*

of maximum dip of the planes and the corners of the spherical triangle.

Blocks in category I cannot move because all the block surface lines are directed upwards towards the rock face (Figs 7.13a & c). Blocks in category II undergo sliding, if unstable, along the single block surface line that has the steepest downward inclination (Figs 7.13b & d). This extreme line, given by L_{min} at an overhanging face and L_{max} at a non-overhanging face, can be either the rotated line of maximum dip of a single plane (giving single plane sliding) or the line of intersection between two planes (giving double plane sliding on the two planes). In the case of single plane sliding, the trend and plunge of the sliding direction are given by the dip direction and dip amount of the plane in question. Where double plane sliding is predicted, the true orientation of the line of intersection can be found either by reversing the rotation ϱ_f for the intersection point or by replotting the planes involved, on an ordinary lower-hemisphere projection. Blocks in category II are more likely to be unstable if the predicted direction of sliding has a steep downward plunge. This occurs for blocks in category IIa when θ_{min} is small, and for blocks in category IIb when θ_{max} is large. Those blocks in category III simply fall vertically from the rock face, if they are unstable (Fig. 7.13e).

7.4.4 Summary and examples

The process of interpreting an inclined hemisphere projection can now be summarised as follows.

(1) Each spherical triangle on the projection is kinematically congruent with the associated tetrahedral block at the given face. A spherical triangle can be regarded as a locus of block surface lines for the associated block. Any block that is deduced to have a sliding mechanism of failure must, if unstable, slide along a block surface line.

(2) The great circle of the rotated horizontal plane divides the projection into two zones: one above and one below the horizontal. The rotated line of maximum dip, D_{fr}, of the rock face serves to differentiate between these zones since it always plots below the horizontal. When this rotated line of maximum dip is placed at the southern azimuth of the net, the original north, south, east and west points are interpreted as up, down, right and left respectively, in the plane of the inclined face.

(3) Any purely geometrical line, represented by a point on the projection, is assumed to be directed outwards towards free air, in an upward direction if it plots above the rotated horizontal plane and downwards if it plots below this plane. The angle of plunge of a given line is the acute angle from that line to the rotated horizontal plane measured along the great circle containing the vertical, N_{hr}.

(4) A valid tetrahedral block, involving one or more additional free faces, can only be formed if the associated spherical triangle constructs the block on the rock mass side of each face.

(5) The inclined hemisphere representation r_r of the resultant force vector r that acts upon a given block can be used to determine the mode of failure of the block, if it is unstable. The direction of r_r, either outwards towards free air or inwards towards the rock mass, depends upon the sense of r and the position of r_r on the inclined hemisphere projection, as summarised in Table 7.1.

(6) The relation between the geometry of a given block and the orientation of the resultant force that acts upon it is expressed in terms of the angle θ counted *internally* from r_r to the point, L, which represents a block surface line on the perimeter of the associated spherical triangle. There will always be one unique point, L_{min}, associated with the minimum value of θ, θ_{min}, and another unique point, L_{max}, associated with the maximum value θ_{max}. There can only ever be up to six possible candidates for L_{min} and L_{max} on a given spherical triangle: one on each of the three planes involved, at the point where each plane is intersected by the great circle that contains both r_r and the rotated normal to the plane; the remaining three candidate points are the corners of the spherical triangle. The values of θ_{min} and θ_{max}, and also the direction and orientation of r_r, are important indicators of how the associated tetrahedral block will behave. The various possible combinations of these values give rise to five different categories of block behaviour as summarised in Table 7.2 and Figure 7.12.

(7) Where blocks are subject only to simple gravitational loading, the resultant force vector on the block acts downwards in a vertical direction, given by N_{hr} on an inclined hemisphere projection. This force is, therefore, directed outwards from any overhanging face and inwards towards the rock mass when the face is non-overhanging. As before, there are only six possible candidates for L_{min} and L_{max} on a given spherical triangle. In this case, blocks that are deduced to be potentially unstable either slide down the block surface line of steepest downward inclination or, alternatively, fall vertically, if unstable. The interpretation of the behaviour of blocks that are subject only to simple gravitational loading is summarised in Table 7.3 and Figure 7.13.

(8) If the predicted direction of sliding for a given block lies on a single plane, then the block will, if unstable, slide on that single plane. If the predicted sliding direction lies at a corner of the spherical triangle then the block will, if unstable, slide on the two planes involved, along their line of intersection, which is represented by the corner. Blocks that are deduced to

have a sliding mode of failure are more likely to be unstable when either θ_{min} is small or θ_{max} is large. If the block under analysis is formed by a valid combination of discontinuity planes and one or more additional free faces, then the sliding direction can never occur in the plane of one of these additional free faces.

The following examples illustrate the interpretation of block behaviour under conditions of simple gravitational loading.

Example 7.3 (Fig. 7.7) Analyse the modes of failure that could be induced by simple gravitational loading of the tetrahedral blocks represented by the spherical triangles on the inclined hemisphere projection in Figure 7.7, constructed for an overhanging face of dip direction/dip amount 120/50. In the case of sliding mechanisms, give the plane(s) of sliding and also the sliding direction.

The first step is to place the rotated line of maximum dip of the rock face, D_{fr}, at the southern azimuth of the net. The rotated vertical, N_{hr}, represents the resultant force vector, which acts downwards on each of the ten tetrahedral blocks given by the ten kinematically congruent spherical triangles on the projection. Since N_{hr} plots below the horizontal plane and represents a force with a downward sense, this resultant force must be directed outwards towards free air (Table 7.1). All blocks must, therefore, belong either to category Ia, IIa or III in Table 7.3. No spherical triangle in Figure 7.7 plots entirely above the horizontal plane, so there are no blocks in category Ia (this is a common occurrence when the rock face is overhanging and has a relatively small angle of dip). There are five spherical triangles that each enclose the rotated vertical direction N_{hr}, and therefore represent category III blocks that can fall vertically from this overhanging face. These falling blocks are the following: 1,2,4 (defined by intersections of planes 1, 2 and 4), 1,2,5, 1,3,5, 2,3,4 and 3,4,5. The five remaining spherical triangles all represent blocks of category IIa which, if unstable, in each case slide outwards along their block surface line, L_{min}, that makes the smallest acute angle, θ_{min}, measured internally from N_{hr}. The spherical triangle defined by the intersection of planes 1, 2 and 3 has a θ_{min} of only 9°, given by the rotated line of maximum dip of plane 3, D_{3r}, which represents L_{min} for the associated block. This block, if unstable, will therefore slide on plane 3, down its line of maximum dip which has a trend/plunge 150/81. Blocks 1,4,5 and 2,4,5 also, if unstable, suffer single plane sliding, the former on plane 4 (325/32) and the latter on plane 5 (048/64). Block 1,3,4 cannot fall vertically since it does not enclose N_{hr}. Plane 1 of this block plots closest to N_{hr} and must, therefore, contain L_{min}. The line of maximum dip, D_{1r}, of this plane is not, however, a block surface line. Conse-

quently L_{min} for this block is the intersection of planes 1 and 3 which gives a θ_{min} of 47°. In this case, the other prime candidate for L_{min}, the intersection between planes 1 and 4, has an angle θ of over 74°. Block 1,3,4 will therefore slide, if unstable, on planes 1 and 3 along their line of intersection which, from an ordinary lower-hemisphere projection, has a trend/plunge 231/43. Block 2,3,5 also, if unstable, undergoes double plane sliding. In this case L_{min} is given by the intersection between planes 2 and 3, which gives a sliding direction of trend/plunge 080/65. The complete analysis of the ten blocks, summarised in Table 7.4, shows that this overhanging rock face could present severe stability problems, not only from falling but also from sliding blocks. The steep inclination of many of the sliding directions would be of particular concern.

Table 7.4 Summary of results for Example 7.3, relating to Figure 7.7.

Block	Sliding planes	Sliding direction if unstable (trend/plunge)
1,2,3	3	150/81
1,2,4	falls vertically	–
1,2,5	falls vertically	–
1,3,4	1 and 3	231/43
1,3,5	falls vertically	–
1,4,5	4	325/32
2,3,4	falls vertically	–
2,3,5	2 and 3	080/65
2,4,5	5	048/64
3,4,5	falls vertically	–

Example 7.4 (Fig. 7.8) Analyse the modes of failure that could be induced by simple gravitational loading of the tetrahedral blocks represented by the spherical triangles on the inclined hemisphere projection in Figure 7.8, constructed for a non-overhanging face of dip direction/dip amount 251/60. Carry out this analysis assuming that plane 5 is a non-overhanging additional free face located on the rock mass side of the main face. In the case of sliding mechanisms, give the plane(s) of sliding and also the sliding direction.

As before, the first step is to place D_{fr} at the southern azimuth of the net. Plane 5, the additional free face, which can be regarded as forming the top of the main non-overhanging face, can only be involved with blocks that are formed on the rock mass side of it. Since plane 5 represents a non-overhanging face, only those spherical triangles constructed below it on the projection are associated with valid tetrahedral blocks. The four spherical triangles formed by planes 1, 2 and 5, planes 1, 3 and 5, planes 2, 3 and 5, and planes 3, 4 and 5 all occur above plane 5 and do not, therefore, represent valid blocks. The six remaining spherical triangles are all associated with valid kinematically feasible tetrahedral blocks at this face. As before, the rotated vertical, N_{hr}, represents the resultant force vector, which acts downwards on each of these blocks. Since, in this case, N_{hr} plots above the horizontal plane and represents a force with a downward sense, this resultant force must be directed inwards towards the rock mass (Table 7.1). All of the six remaining blocks must, therefore, belong to either category Ib or IIb in Table 7.3.

Clearly, no blocks can fall vertically from this non-overhanging face. The spherical triangle formed by the intersection of planes 1, 2 and 3 plots entirely above the rotated horizontal plane, so the associated block must be of category Ib. This means that all the block surface lines are directed upwards towards free air and so the block cannot slide or fall from the face under simple gravitational loading. The five remaining spherical triangles all represent blocks of category IIb which, if unstable, in each case slide outwards along their block surface line, L_{max}, that makes the largest obtuse angle, θ_{max}, measured internally from N_{hr}. It is relatively easy to find L_{max} for a given spherical triangle, since it is simply the block surface line that plots furthest below the rotated horizontal plane. The spherical triangle formed by planes 1, 2 and 4 plots partly below the horizontal, with plane 4 forming the lower margin of the block. The line L_{max} for this spherical triangle, given by the rotated line of maximum dip of plane 4, D_{4r}, has a θ_{max} of 131°. Two other candidates for L_{max} on this spherical triangle, the intersection between planes 1 and 4 and the intersection between planes 2 and 4, have θ values of only 123° and 127° respectively. By definition, the line of maximum dip of a given plane will always be of steeper inclination than any other line in the plane. Block 1,2,4, if unstable, will therefore slide on plane 4, down its line of maximum dip of trend/plunge 244/41. Blocks 1,3,4 and 1,4,5, if unstable, also slide on plane 4 in this direction. Plane 4 also forms the lower margin of block 2,3,4 and must, therefore, contain L_{max}. The line of maximum dip, D_{4r}, of this plane is not, however, a block surface line. Consequently, L_{max} for this block is the intersection of planes 2 and 4 which gives a θ_{max} of 127° and which, from an ordinary lower-hemisphere projection, has a trend/plunge 273/37. Block 2,4,5, if unstable, also slides on planes 2 and 4 in this direction. The complete analysis for this example, summarised in Table 7.5, confirms that the additional free face (plane 5) never forms a sliding plane. This must always be the case because sliding requires a rock-to-rock interface. The results in this table suggest that planes 2 and 4 are of critical importance in controlling the stability of rock blocks exposed at the non-overhanging face.

Table 7.5 Summary of results for Example 7.4, relating to Figure 7.8.

Block	Sliding planes	Sliding direction if unstable (trend/plunge)
1,2,3	directed upwards	–
1,2,4	4	244/41
1,2,5	not valid	–
1,3,4	4	244/41
1,3,5	not valid	–
1,4,5	4	244/41
2,3,4	2 and 4	273/37
2,3,5	not valid	–
2,4,5	2 and 4	273/37
3,4,5	not valid	–

Exercises

In each exercise, construct an inclined hemisphere projection for the given rock face and the various discontinuity orientations specified. Analyse the modes of failure that could be induced by simple gravitational loading of the tetrahedral blocks represented by the spherical triangles on each resulting projection. In the case of sliding mechanisms, give the plane(s) of sliding and also the sliding direction.

7.1 Overhanging rock face, dip direction/dip amount 292/35.

Discontinuity	Dip direction (deg)	Dip amount (deg)
1	272	72
2	018	68
3	092	72
4	120	27
5	140	48

7.2 Non-overhanging rock face, dip direction/dip amount 218/75.

Discontinuity	Dip direction (deg)	Dip amount (deg)
1	165	48
2	231	62
3	337	71
4	109	56
5	192	30

Specify those blocks that would become invalid if plane 5 were a non-overhanging additional free face.

7.3 Vertical rock face, dip direction/dip amount 170/90. Rock mass lies on the northern side of the face.

Discontinuity	Dip direction (deg)	Dip amount (deg)
1	019	65
2	335	48
3	306	71
4	237	54
5	104	32

7.4 Non-overhanging rock face, dip direction/dip amount 310/55.

Discontinuity	Dip direction (deg)	Dip amount (deg)
1	015	50
2	258	39
3	170	64
4	303	46

The top of the rock face is marked by an additional, non-overhanging free face of dip direction/dip amount 333/18.

Answers to these exercises are given on page 123.

8 Analysis of the stability of rigid blocks

8.1 Introduction

The construction and interpretation of inclined hemisphere projections, explained in the previous chapter, provides a valuable tool for the assessment of kinematic feasibility and potential failure mechanisms of tetrahedral blocks exposed at an overhanging or non-overhanging rock face of any orientation. An important feature of this assessment is the classification of each kinematically feasible tetrahedral block into one of five different categories, according to its ability to fall or slide from the rock mass (Section 7.4). This classification is largely based upon the orientation and sense of the resultant force vector **r** that acts upon the block. This resultant force depends not only upon the weight of the block but also upon any water pressures acting on the planes bounding the block and any additional external factors such as foundations sited on the block, rock bolts and seismic effects. Methods for determining the weight of a given block and thereby determining the resultant force vector **r** are explained in Sections 8.2 and 8.3. Before proceeding with this, however, it is necessary to set out the criteria by which the stability of a block in a given category will be assessed.

Any block that is classified as category I in Tables 7.2 or 7.3 can never become unstable unless the forces acting upon the block are changed. Any block that is classified as category III is free to move in the direction of the resultant force vector, which induces tensile normal forces across each of the discontinuity planes that delimit the block. In most rock mechanics studies, discontinuity planes are assumed to have zero tensile strength. This assumption means that any category III block will be actually unstable unless an adequate additional reaction to the resultant force vector can be provided. This reaction would usually take the form of rock bolts or some other rock support system. Blocks in category II are deduced to fail, if they are unstable, by sliding either on a single plane or along the line of intersection between two planes. Whether blocks in this category are actually unstable or not depends upon the shear strength(s) of the sliding plane(s) and also the forces acting on the plane(s). These forces depend partly upon the orientation(s) of the plane(s) involved and partly upon the resultant force vector that acts upon the block. Much of the remainder of this chapter will be devoted to analysing the stability of these category II blocks, which can develop sliding failure mechanisms.

A simple, and widely accepted, model for the shear strength of a discontinuity plane is based partly upon the magnitude $|\mathbf{n}|$ of the effective compressive normal force **n** acting across the plane. This force is called an effective force to emphasise the fact that it represents the combined effects of all relevant forces, in particular gravitational loading and the effects of water pressures. The shear strength model assumes that, when **n** is compressive across the discontinuity plane, the maximum shearing force, S_m, that this discontinuity can sustain without suffering significant shear displacement is given by

$$S_m = c'A + |\mathbf{n}| \tan \phi' \qquad (8.1)$$

where c' is the average cohesive strength, which is assumed to act over the area A of the interface, and ϕ' is the angle of friction. The 'prime' symbol attached to these parameters denotes that they are effective shear strength parameters. If **n** is tensile across the discontinuity surface, then separation occurs and the sliding mechanism does not operate. The effective strength parameter c', which is a measure of the ability of the discontinuity plane to resist shearing at zero normal stress, depends largely upon the nature of any fill or cementing material within the discontinuity aperture. In some cases, however, an apparent cohesion can be produced where a clean discontinuity surface is relatively uneven, thereby inducing shearing through intact elements of rock material even at low normal stress. Although peak cohesive strength can range from zero to over 700 kN/m^2, it usually lies between 5 and 50 kN/m^2 for discontinuities in most rock types. The effective angle of friction is dependent upon the mineralogy and roughness of the sliding surfaces. Again, although the peak friction angle can range from $7.5°$ to over $40°$, it usually lies between $15°$ and $35°$ for most discontinuity types. It is important that the magnitudes of the effective shear strength parameters for a given discontinuity plane are determined from a comprehensive programme of field and/or laboratory tests. It is recommended that the reader who wishes to learn more about the theoretical and experimental aspects of discontinuity shear strength should consult the texts by Hoek and Bray (1981) and Brady and Brown (1985).

The shear strength model, embodied in Equation 8.1, will be used throughout the remainder of this chapter. The magnitude $|\mathbf{s}|$ of the maximum shearing force **s** on a given single discontinuity plane can never, under stable conditions, exceed the value S_m given by Equation 8.1. Consequently, if an analysis of a given block predicts that $|\mathbf{s}|$ will exceed S_m on the single plane of sliding, then the block is regarded as unstable by the assumed sliding failure mechanism. The ratio $S_m/|\mathbf{s}|$ is, therefore, a measure of the stability of the block. When this ratio exceeds unity the block is stable; larger values of this ratio imply a greater degree of stability. Indices of stability such as this are usually called factors of safety and referred to by the parameter F. In this case, for single plane sliding

$$F = S_m/|\mathbf{s}| = \frac{c'A + |\mathbf{n}|\tan\phi'}{|\mathbf{s}|} \qquad (8.2)$$

Where double plane sliding is predicted, the relevant value of shear force $\mathbf{s}$ is that acting along the line of intersection of the two planes involved. In this case if the effective strength parameters, areas and effective compressive normal forces are c'_1, ϕ'_1, A_1 and $\mathbf{n}_1$ on the first plane and c'_2, ϕ'_2, A_2 and $\mathbf{n}_2$ on the second plane of sliding, then the factor of safety F is defined as

$$F = \frac{c'_1 A_1 + |\mathbf{n}_1|\tan\phi'_1 + c'_2 A_2 + |\mathbf{n}_2|\tan\phi'_2}{|\mathbf{s}|} \qquad (8.3)$$

which embodies the implicit assumption that both planes have the same factor of safety.

It must be emphasised that the factors of safety defined in Equations 8.2 and 8.3 are merely indices of stability that are dependent upon the assumed failure mechanisms and force distribution. Factors of safety defined in other ways could well differ when F is not equal to unity.

It is now possible to list the information required to carry out a stability analysis of a kinematically feasible tetrahedral block:

(a) The orientation magnitude and sense of the resultant force vector $\mathbf{r}$ that acts upon the block. This depends upon

    (i) the weight of the block;
    (ii) forces generated by water pressures acting on the planes bounding the block;
    (iii) external forces such as foundation loads, rock bolt loads and seismic forces.

This information is sufficient to deduce the category of block behaviour. Blocks in category I are stable; those in category III are unstable, whatever the magnitude of $\mathbf{r}$. The following information is required to determine the stability of blocks in category II, which are deduced to have a sliding mechanism, if unstable:

(b) The effective shear strength parameters, c' and ϕ', the area(s) and orientation(s) of the plane(s) that is (are) deduced to be involved in sliding.

The information required for the stability analysis of a block is derived from several different sources. The shear strength parameters are obtained from field or laboratory tests. External forces such as foundation and rock bolt loads can be found by analysing the external structures involved. Water pressures on the discontinuity planes are more difficult to determine. They can be either measured directly or estimated from some numerical or analytical model of water flow near the block. Since a detailed discussion of water flow in discontinuous rock masses is beyond the scope of this book, relatively simple idealisations of water pressure distributions will be adopted in order to provide general illustrations of the stability analyses. The weight of the block is determined from its volume and unit weight. The volume of the block and the areas of the block surface triangles[1] are determined from the geometry of the associated kinematically congruent spherical triangle. It is in this geometrical analysis that the inclined hemisphere projection finds its most important and valuable application.

8.2 Geometrical analysis of a spherical triangle

Figure 8.1 shows a spherical triangle that is kinematically congruent with a tetrahedral block whose stability is being investigated. Although the inclined hemisphere projection in this figure has been constructed for an overhanging face of dip direction/dip amount 216/65, the geometrical analysis described below is entirely general and can be carried out on any spherical triangle on an inclined hemisphere projection constructed for an overhanging or non-overhanging face of any orientation. The basis of this geometrical analysis is to construct a scaled plan view of the associated tetrahedral block, projected onto the rock face and viewed in a direction normal to the face looking out towards free air from within the rock mass. In order to do this it is first necessary to construct the following diametral lines on the inclined hemisphere projection:

(1) The diametral lines joining the ends of the great circles of the three planes, here referred to as planes 1, 2 and 3, that define the tetrahedral block. These lines, which give the orientations of the traces produced where each plane intersects the rock face, define the geometry of the face triangle[1] of the block.
(2) The diametral lines that pass through the corners of the spherical triangle. These lines give the orientations of the traces produced where the normal planes passing through the block corners intersect the rock face.
(3) The diametral line joining the ends of the great circle of the rotated horizontal plane. This gives a horizontal reference line in the plane of the rock face.

---

[1] See definitions at the beginning of Section 7.4.

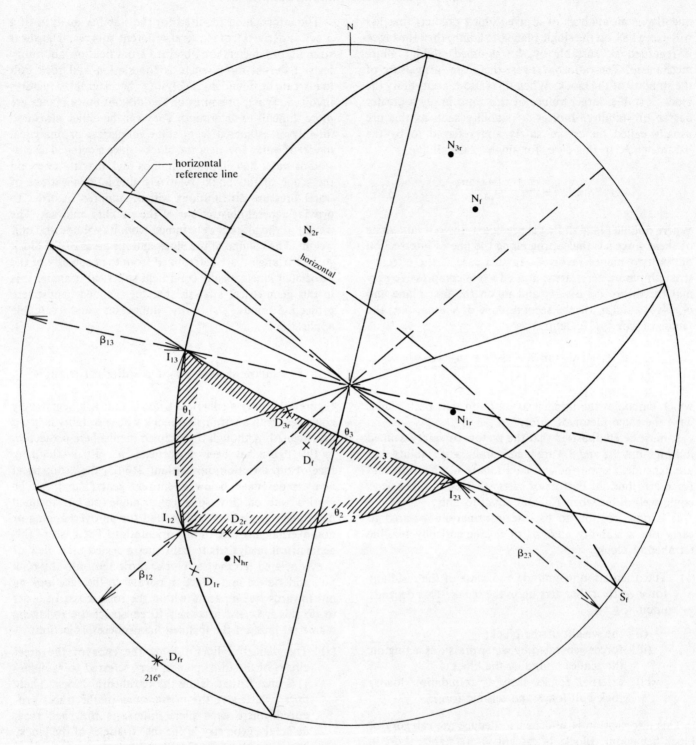

Figure 8.1 Inclined hemisphere projection with diametral construction lines.

Before constructing the scaled plan view, it is important to bear in mind that the properties of kinematic congruence ensure that the relative locations of the great circles on the spherical triangle are the same as those of their respective planes on the associated block. In the example in Figure 8.1, when D_{fr} is at the southern azimuth of the net, plane 1 forms the lower left-hand boundary, plane 2 forms the lower right-hand boundary and plane 3 the top of the block when it is viewed looking out towards free air from within the rock mass. The traces of the planes that form the face triangle must, therefore, have the same relative locations as their associated great circles on the spherical triangle.

The scaled plan view is constructed on a separate sheet of tracing paper. The first step is to draw a straight line on this paper to represent the horizontal reference line in the plane of the rock face as shown in Figure 8.2. It is now necessary to define some suitable scale. This scale is controlled by the size of the block being studied. In the absence of detailed information concerning the location and size of the discontinuities involved, the approach adopted here is to analyse the largest block that could be released from the rock face. There will always be just one limiting dimension of the rock face that constrains the size of the face triangle for a given block. This limiting dimension may be the width of the face, measured along the strike line, or perhaps the 'height' measured along the line of maximum dip. A scaled representation of the rock face, incorporating the limiting dimension, is constructed on the tracing paper at the correct orientation relative to the horizontal reference line. This will represent a window within which the face triangle must be constructed. In Figure 8.2 the limiting dimension of the face is its width, which is 8 m measured along the strike line. In this case, the extreme left and right corners of the face triangle of the largest possible block must occur at the left and right margins of the face window respectively. To commence the construction, an arbitrary point is selected on the left-hand margin of the face window. This point, which represents the intersection of planes 1 and 3, is superimposed at the exact centre of the inclined hemisphere projection in Figure 8.1 and then the overlay is rotated until it is the correct way up, with its horizontal reference line parallel to that on the projection. This process of orientating the overlay is greatly facilitated if the starting point for construction is selected so that it lies close to, or actually on, the horizontal reference line of the overlay, as shown in Figure 8.2. The diametral lines associated with planes 1 and 3 on the projection can now be traced onto the overlay, so that they radiate from the initial point and run across the face window.

The right-hand corner of the face triangle occurs at the point where the line associated with plane 3 intersects the right-hand margin of the face window. This point is now placed at the centre of the projection and the overlay is

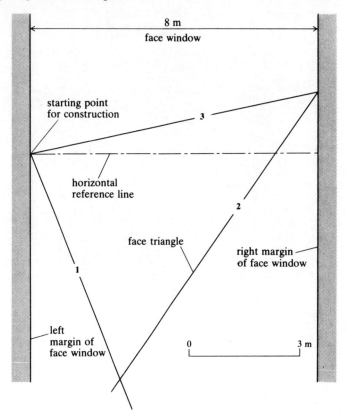

Figure 8.2 Construction of face triangle.

again rotated to its correct orientation. This reorientation of the overlay can now be achieved simply by ensuring that the line associated with plane 3 is correctly superimposed on its diametral line on the projection. The diametral line associated with plane 2 can now be traced off to complete the construction of the face triangle as shown in Figure 8.2.

The face triangle constructed in Figure 8.2 can be regarded as the base of the tetrahedral block viewed from within the rock mass. It is now necessary to construct a scaled plan view of the block corners, which define the location of the block apex. To do this, one corner of the face triangle is placed at the centre of the projection in figure 8.1. With the overlay correctly orientated, the diametral line on the projection relating to the associated block corner is traced off. This process is repeated for the other corners of the face triangle to give three lines that represent the plan positions of the block corners in the plane of the rock face. These three lines intersect to define the plan position of the block apex, as shown in Figure 8.3. An alternative method for locating the block apex is simply to position the scaled plan view on top of the projection so that the corners of the face triangle lie on the diametral lines constructed through the same corners of the associated spherical triangle. When this is done, the centre of the projection gives the location of the block apex on the scaled plan view. When the apex location has been

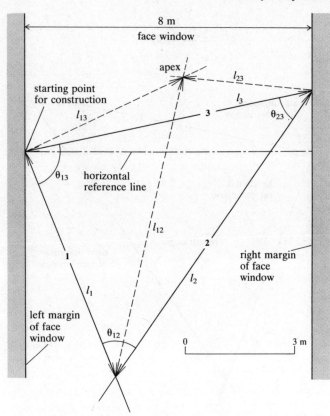

Figure 8.3 Scaled plan view of tetrahedral block.

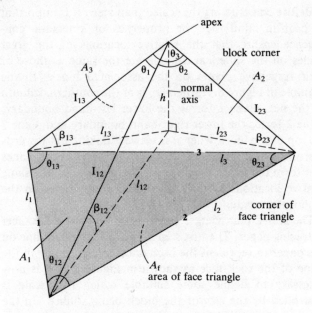

Figure 8.4 Geometrical properties of a tetrahedral block.

found, the construction is complete and can be used, with the associated spherical triangle, to provide all the required information concerning the geometry of the block. It is worth noting that the block in this illustration has an external normal axis; this means that the apex must plot outside the face triangle on the scaled plan view.

The lengths l_1, l_2 and l_3 of the three sides of the face triangle and also the lengths l_{12}, l_{23} and l_{13} of the three block corners *projected onto the rock face* can be scaled directly from the plan view as shown in Figure 8.3. The corner angles of the face triangle θ_{12}, θ_{23} and θ_{13} can also be measured directly from the diagram.

Additional angular measurements are taken from the spherical triangle on the inclined hemisphere projection in Figure 8.1. The acute angles β_{12}, β_{23} and β_{13}, measured in a normal plane between each block corner and the rock face, are measured in exactly the same way as if they were angles of plunge on an ordinary lower-hemisphere projection, each angle being measured from the appropriate corner of the spherical triangle along a diametral line to the perimeter of the projection as shown in Figure 8.1. The solid angles θ_1, θ_2 and θ_3 between each pair of block corners are measured in planes 1, 2 and 3 respectively. These angles are counted in the usual way along the appropriate great circles between the corners of the spherical triangle, again as shown in Figure 8.1.

Figure 8.4 shows a three-dimensional view of the

tetrahedral block analysed in Figures 8.1 to 8.3. This illustrates the important point that l_{12}, l_{23} and l_{13} are not the true lengths of the three block corners but are their apparent lengths when projected onto the rock face. The true lengths of these block corners are, therefore, given by $l_{12}/\cos\beta_{12}$, $l_{23}/\cos\beta_{23}$ and $l_{13}/\cos\beta_{13}$ respectively. The area of each face of the tetrahedral block can now be found by simple geometry. The area, A_f, of the face triangle can be found by taking any pair of adjacent sides and their included angle as follows

$$A_f = \tfrac{1}{2}l_1l_2\sin\theta_{12} = \tfrac{1}{2}l_2l_3\sin\theta_{23} = \tfrac{1}{2}l_1l_3\sin\theta_{13} \quad (8.4)$$

The areas of the three block surface triangles are found, in a similar way, from the true lengths of the block corners and the appropriate included angles as follows

$$A_1 = \frac{1}{2}\left(\frac{l_{12}}{\cos\beta_{12}}\,\frac{l_{13}}{\cos\beta_{13}}\right)\sin\theta_1$$

$$A_2 = \frac{1}{2}\left(\frac{l_{12}}{\cos\beta_{12}}\,\frac{l_{23}}{\cos\beta_{23}}\right)\sin\theta_2 \quad (8.5)$$

$$A_3 = \frac{1}{2}\left(\frac{l_{13}}{\cos\beta_{13}}\,\frac{l_{23}}{\cos\beta_{23}}\right)\sin\theta_3$$

The distance from the block apex to the rock face, measured along the normal axis, is here termed the block height, h. This height can be found from the projected lengths of any one of the block corners, as follows

$$h = l_{12}\tan\beta_{12} = l_{23}\tan\beta_{23} = l_{13}\tan\beta_{13} \quad (8.6)$$

The volume V of the block is given by

$$V = A_f h/3 \qquad (8.7)$$

The following examples serve to illustrate this geometrical analysis. As with all graphical methods, the precision of the results depends upon the care taken in the construction. Readers who work carefully through these examples, and also the exercises at the end of this chapter, should expect their values to lie within $\pm 5\%$ of the results given.

Example 8.1 (Figs 8.5 & 8.6) Three persistent, planar discontinuity sets, with dip directions/dip amounts (1) 138/51, (2) 355/40 and (3) 219/67, are known to occur in the vicinity of the horizontal, overhanging planar roof of an excavation in sedimentary rock. This roof, which is rectangular in shape, measures 10 m by 6 m and is orientated with its longer dimension at an azimuth of 025°. Determine the geometrical properties of the largest tetrahedral block, formed by the three discontinuity sets, that could in theory fall or slide from this roof under simple gravitational loading.

The discontinuities in this example are, in fact, the same as those considered earlier in connection with Figure 7.3. Since in this case the rock face is horizontal and overhanging, an ordinary lower-hemisphere projection will generate the kinematically congruent spherical triangle for the tetrahedral block. The spherical triangle on the resulting projection, in Figure 8.5, encloses the vertical direction, N_h, at the centre of the projection, which in this case, under simple gravitational loading, represents the resultant force vector that acts upon the associated block. This means that the block is classified as category III in Table 7.3 and could, therefore, fall vertically from the excavation roof. The geometry of this block, illustrated earlier in Figure 7.3a, confirms that the block has an internal normal axis.

Six diametral construction lines, referred to earlier in this section, are drawn on the projection: three joining the ends of the great circles of the three discontinuity planes and three passing through the corners of the spherical triangle, as shown in Figure 8.5. In this particular example the great circle of the horizontal plane is given by the perimeter of the projection. In view of this, it is convenient to construct the diametral horizontal reference line at an azimuth 025°, corresponding to the longer dimension of the excavation roof.

Figure 8.6 shows an orientated scaled plan view of the rectangular excavation roof. Inspection of the spherical triangle in Figure 8.5 suggests that the corner of the face triangle formed by planes 2 and 3 will touch the western margin of the roof, and the corner formed by planes 1 and 2 will touch the eastern margin when the largest possible tetrahedral block is constructed. The 10 m length of the roof is not a limiting dimension in this case. An arbitrary starting point for the construction is marked about halfway along the western margin of the roof. This point, which now represents the corner of the face triangle formed by planes 2 and 3, is superimposed at the exact centre of the projection. The overlay is then rotated until the longer margin of the roof lies on the reference line of azimuth 025°. The diametral lines associated with planes 2 and 3 can now be traced off and extended across the full width of the roof. The point where the line for plane 2 intersects the eastern margin of the roof represents the corner of the face triangle formed by planes 1 and 2. This point can now be placed over the centre of the projection, and, with the overlay reorientated, the line associated with plane 1 can be traced off to complete the face triangle. Any attempt to construct the corner of the face triangle formed by planes 1 and 3 at the eastern margin of the face would place the corner of the face triangle formed by planes 1 and 2 beyond the face, within the rock mass.

The plan position of the block corner formed by planes 1 and 2 is constructed by placing the associated corner of the face triangle at the centre of the projection, reorientating the overlay, and then tracing off the diametral line relating to the associated block corner. This process, when repeated for the two other block corners, generates three lines that converge to a point which gives the plan position of the block apex. This gives a valuable check since the area of the triangle of error formed by these converging lines is a measure of any imprecision in the construction. The apex of this block, which has an internal normal axis, plots within the face triangle on the scaled plan view.

In practice, it is only possible to make one type of gross error during the construction: this is to construct mistakenly the scaled plan view of the alternative block, illustrated earlier in Figure 7.3b. This error can always be detected because the resulting block is not kinematically congruent with the spherical triangle on the projection. Apart from this, the construction is essentially an automatic process that is largely self-checking.

The dimensions of the face triangle in Figure 8.6 are $l_1 = 4.85$ m, $l_2 = 6.90$ m and $l_3 = 4.20$ m, scaled off to the nearest 0.05 m. The projected lengths of the block corners are $l_{12} = 4.55$ m, $l_{23} = 3.15$ m and $l_{13} = 1.25$ m. The corner angles of the face triangle are $\theta_{12} = 37°$, $\theta_{23} = 44°$ and $\theta_{13} = 99°$; these angles should, of course, add up to 180°. The angles between each block corner and the rock face, measured on the projection in Figure 8.5, are $\beta_{12} = 18°$, $\beta_{23} = 25°$ and $\beta_{13} = 50°$. The solid angles between each pair of block corners, also measured on this projection are $\theta_1 = 80°$, $\theta_2 = 112°$ and $\theta_3 = 98°$ measured in planes 1, 2 and 3 respectively. The three values for the area, A_f, of the face triangle, given by Equations 8.4, are 10.07, 10.07 and 10.06 m^2. The areas of each block surface triangle, given by Equations 8.5 are $A_1 = 4.58$ m^2, $A_2 = 7.71$ m^2 and $A_3 = 3.35$ m^2. The three values for the block height h, given by Equations 8.6, are 1.48, 1.47 and 1.49 m. Putting

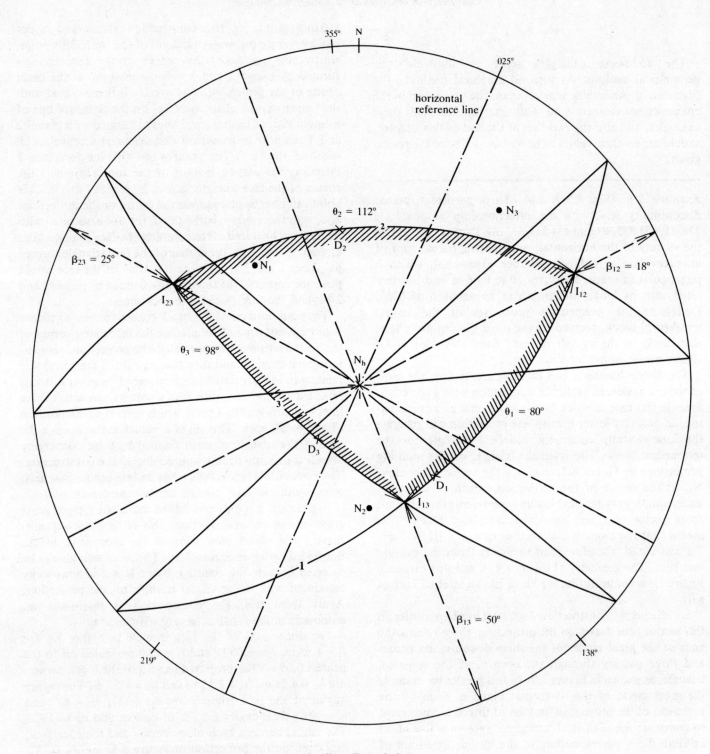

Figure 8.5 Hemispherical projection with diametral construction lines (Example 8.1).

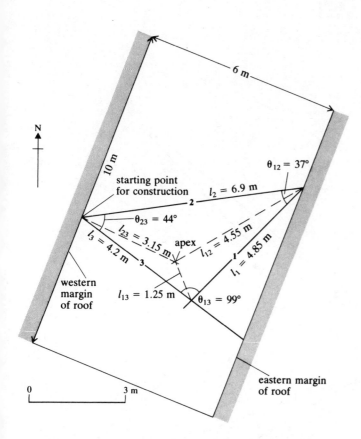

Figure 8.6 Scaled plan view of tetrahedral block (Example 8.1).

the mean values for A_f and h into Equation 8.7 gives a block volume of $V = 4.97$ m^3. A reasonable value for the unit weight of a sedimentary rock material is 25 kN/m^3. This means that the block would have a weight of 124.2 kN and would require a support pressure of only 12.3 kN/m^2, distributed over the face triangle, to keep it in place. This support pressure could, for example, be provided by rock bolts anchored beyond the block, at a distance of 2 to 3 m above the excavation roof.

The volume V of a given tetrahedron is proportional to the cube of any characteristic linear dimension, l. Introducing a geometrical constant, k_v, gives the following relation

$$V = k_v \, l^3 \qquad (8.8)$$

The parameter k_v is a dimensionless constant that depends only upon the orientations of the four planes involved in the tetrahedron. In many cases a convenient characteristic dimension, l, is the width of the face within which the face triangle exactly fits. In Example 8.1, taking l as the width of the roof, when $l = 6$ m the block volume V is 4.97 m^3 and so for this block $k_v = 0.0230$. If the width of the roof were increased to say, 9 m, the volume of the largest block formed by the same three discontinuity orien-

tations would increase. Setting $l = 9$ m in Equation 8.8 gives the new volume as 16.77 m^3. This assumes of course, that the size of the larger block is not constrained by any other dimensions of the face.

The area A of one particular face of a given tetrahedron is proportional to the square of any characteristic linear dimension, l. Again, introducing a dimensionless geometrical constant, k_a, gives the following relation:

$$A = k_a \, l^2 \qquad (8.9)$$

In Example 8.1, and again taking l as the width of the roof, when $l = 6$ m the area of the face triangle is 10.07 m^2 and so for this particular face $k_a = 0.2797$. If l were increased to 9 m, the area of the face triangle of this particular block shape would increase to 22.66 m^2. The largest block exposed at this 9 m face would require, therefore, a support pressure of 18.5 kN/m^2. In general, when blocks of category III are subject only to simple gravitational loading, the required support pressure, p_s, is given by

$$p_s = \frac{\gamma k_v \, l}{k_a} \qquad (8.10)$$

where, in this case, k_v is the volumetric geometrical constant, k_a is the areal geometrical constant for the face triangle and l is the characteristic linear dimension. As before, γ is the unit weight of the rock material. This shows that the required support pressure increases linearly with the size of the rock face. Finally, any linear dimension of a given tetrahedral block is directly proportional to any characteristic linear dimension. The new block height h in the above example is, therefore, 2.22 m for a 9 m wide roof. It is only necessary to construct a scaled plan view of a given block for one characteristic linear dimension, since the volume and surface area of the block associated with any other characteristic dimension can be found from Equations 8.8 and 8.9.

Example 8.2 (Figs 8.7 & 8.8) Three persistent, planar discontinuity sets, with dip directions/dip amounts (1) 185/54, (2) 325/32 and (3) 048/64, are known to occur in the vicinity of an overhanging face of dip direction/dip amount 120/50. Determine the geometrical properties of the largest tetrahedral block, formed by the three discontinuity sets, that could in theory fall or slide from this face under simple gravitational loading if the width of the face measured along its strike is 5 m.

The discontinuity sets 1, 2 and 3 in this example are respectively sets 1, 4 and 5 from Examples 7.1 and 7.3, previously illustrated in Figure 7.7. This figure can be used to give the inclined hemisphere projection for the current example since the overhanging rock face also has the same orientation. The resulting inclined hemisphere projection,

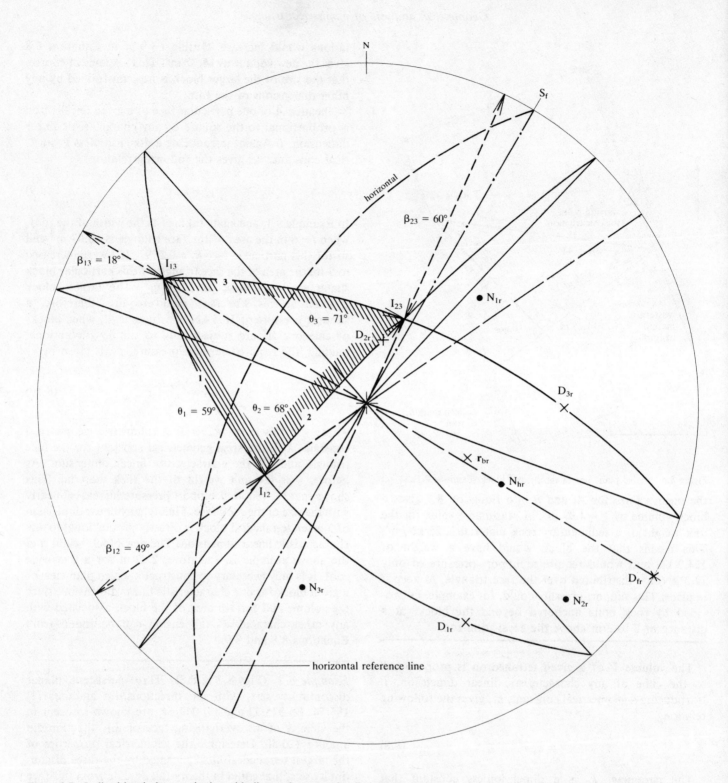

Figure 8.7 Inclined hemisphere projection with diametral construction lines (Example 8.2).

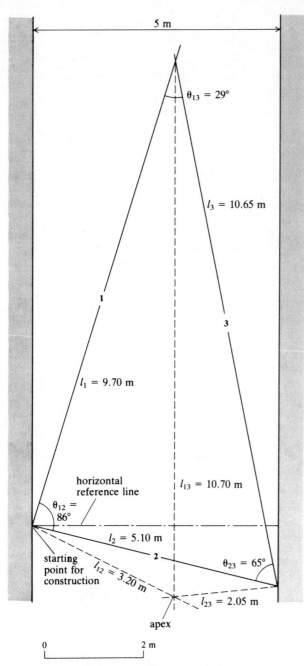

5 m

$\theta_{13} = 29°$

$l_3 = 10.65$ m

1

3

$l_1 = 9.70$ m

horizontal
reference line

$l_{13} = 10.70$ m

$\theta_{12} =$
$86°$

$l_2 = 5.10$ m

starting
point for
construction

$l_{12} = 3.20$ m

2

$\theta_{23} = 65°$

$l_{23} = 2.05$ m

apex

0   2 m

Figure 8.8 Scaled plan view of tetrahedral block (Example 8.2).

at a rock face 5 m wide. The dimensions of the face triangle in this figure are $l_1 = 9.70$ m, $l_2 = 5.10$ m and $l_3 = 10.65$ m. The projected lengths of the block corners are $l_{12} = 3.20$ m, $l_{23} = 2.05$ m and $l_{13} = 10.70$ m. The corner angles of the face triangles are $\theta_{12} = 86°$, $\theta_{23} = 65°$ and $\theta_{13} = 29°$. The angles between each block corner and the rock face, measured on the projection in Figure 8.7, are $\beta_{12} = 49°$, $\beta_{23} = 60°$ and $\beta_{13} = 18°$. Finally, the solid angles between the block corners, also measured on this projection, are $\theta_1 = 59°$, $\theta_2 = 68°$ and $\theta_3 = 71°$ measured in planes 1, 2 and 3 respectively. The three values for the area, A_f, of the face triangle, given by Equations 8.4, are 24.67, 24.61 and 25.04 m². The areas of each block surface triangle, given by Equations 8.5, are $A_1 = 23.52$ m², $A_2 = 9.27$ m² and $A_3 = 21.81$ m². The three values for the block height h, given by Equations 8.6, are 3.68, 3.55 and 3.48 m. As before, the mean values of A_f and h are input to Equation 8.7 to give, in this case, a block volume $V = 29.48$ m³.

In some cases the volume of the largest kinematically feasible block at a given face is constrained not by the size of the face but by the size of one of the discontinuities that forms the block. This is illustrated in the next example.

Example 8.3 (Figs 8.9 & 8.10) Two planar discontinuities, with dip directions/dip amounts (1) 102/66 and (2) 223/50, intersect each other and the face of a non-overhanging rock slope of dip direction/dip amount 163/58. The rock slope has a top formed by an additional non-overhanging free face of dip direction/dip amount 184/10, which intersects the two discontinuities to form a kinematically feasible tetrahedral block. The side of the face triangle of this block formed by the intersection of plane 1 with the slope face has an observed length of 10 m. Determine the potential sliding direction of the tetrahedral block under simple gravitational loading and calculate the geometrical properties of the block.

In this example it is first necessary to construct the inclined hemisphere projection for the non-overhanging rock face. The top of the rock slope is referred to as plane 3 on the resulting projection, which is shown in Figure 8.9. The block associated with the spherical triangle in this figure is valid, since the top of the rock slope (plane 3) forms the upper margin of the spherical triangle. Under simple gravitational loading this block is classified as category IIb and will, if unstable, slide along L_{max}, which in this case is the line of intersection between planes 1 and 2 of trend/plunge 173/37. The scaled plan view of the block in this example is shown in Figure 8.10, constructed so that the side of the face triangle formed by plane 1 has a length of 10 m. The dimensions of the face triangle in this figure are $l_1 = 10.00$ m (given), $l_2 = 11.80$ m and $l_3 = 6.85$ m. The projected lengths of the block corners are $l_{12} = 15.50$ m,

complete with diametral construction lines, is shown in Figure 8.7. The diametral line, constructed through the point of intersection of planes 1 and 3 in this figure, also by chance passes through N_{hr} and D_{fr}. Coincidences such as this are surprisingly common and are best ignored. Under simple gravitational loading, the block associated with the spherical triangle in Figure 8.7 is classified as category IIa and will, if unstable, slide along L_{min}, which in this case is the line of maximum dip of plane 2 of dip direction/dip amount 325/32. The scaled plan view of the block in this example is shown in Figure 8.8, constructed

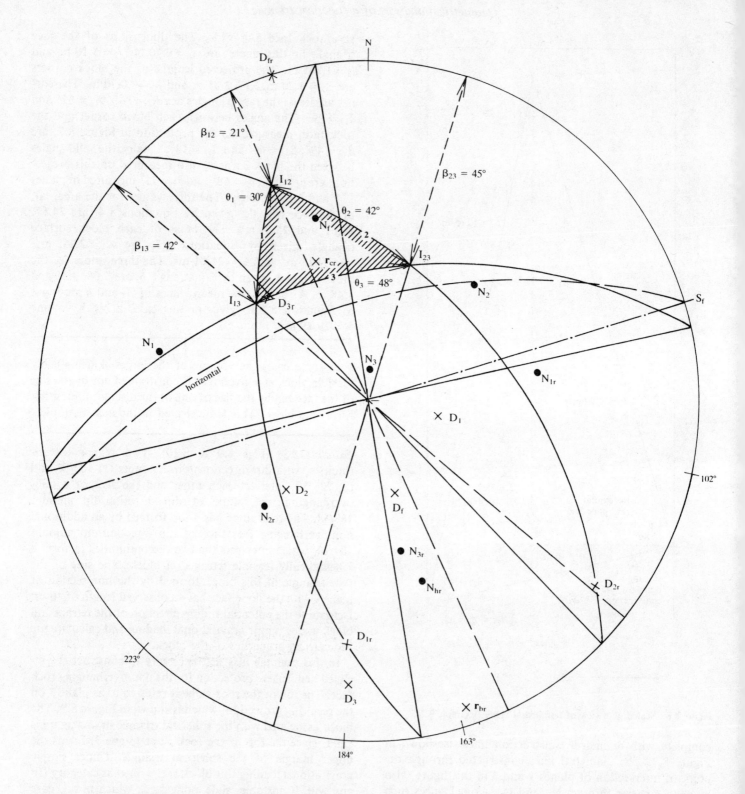

Figure 8.9 Inclined hemisphere projection with diametral construction lines (Example 8.3).

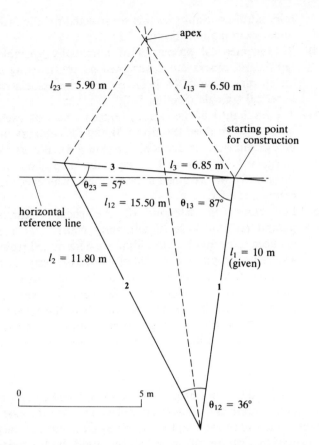

Figure 8.10 Scaled plan view of tetrahedral block (Example 8.3).

$l_{23} = 5.90$ m and $l_{13} = 6.50$ m. The corner angles of the face triangle are $\theta_{12} = 36°$, $\theta_{23} = 57°$ and $\theta_{13} = 87°$. The angles between each block corner and the rock face, measured on the projection in Figure 8.9, are $\beta_{12} = 21°$, $\beta_{23} = 45°$ and $\beta_{13} = 42°$. The solid angles between the block corners on this projection are $\theta_1 = 30°$, $\theta_2 = 42°$ and $\theta_3 = 48°$. The three values for the area, A_f, of the face triangle, given by Equations 8.4, are 34.68, 33.89 and 34.20 m². The areas of each block surface triangle, given by Equations 8.5, are $A_1 = 36.30$ m², $A_2 = 46.35$ m² and $A_3 = 27.12$ m². The three values of block height h, given by Equations 8.6, are 5.95, 5.90 and 5.85 m. As before, the mean values of A_f and h are input to Equation 8.7 to give, in this case, a block volume $V = 67.37$ m³.

8.3 Determination of block stability

In order to determine whether a given block is likely to be unstable, it is first necessary to determine the orientation, magnitude and sense of the resultant **r** of the various forces that act upon the block. This is done using the methods explained in Chapter 6, and in particular Section 6.3. This resultant force can then be transferred to the inclined hemisphere projection to determine the category of block

behaviour according to Table 7.2. Blocks in category I are assumed to be stable and to have, in theory, an infinite factor of safety. Those in category III are assumed to be unstable, with a theoretical factor of safety of zero. Blocks in category II are assumed to exhibit, if unstable, either a single plane or double plane translational sliding mechanism. In this case, it is necessary to decompose the resultant force **r** to find its normal and shear components on the plane(s) of sliding. This is done using the methods explained in Section 6.4. The normal and shear components of force, together with the appropriate effective shear strength parameters, are input to either Equation 8.2 or 8.3, whichever is appropriate, to determine the factor of safety of the block.

In most cases, the largest single force that acts upon any given block is the weight vector, **g**. This always has a vertical orientation, a downward sense and a magnitude given by γV, where γ is the unit weight of the rock material and V is the volume of the block. Methods for calculating V were explained in the previous section. Other external forces, such as rock bolt loads, are determined by analysing the structures involved. Water pressures, acting on the discontinuity planes bounding a given block, can have a dramatic influence on block stability. In some cases water pressures can even change the category of block behaviour from that which would have been deduced on the basis of simple gravitational loading. The magnitude of the force vector **h** generated by an average positive water pressure $\bar{p}$ acting over a discontinuity plane of area A is given by $|\mathbf{h}|$ as follows

$$|\mathbf{h}| = \bar{p}A \qquad (8.11)$$

This force always acts along the normal to the discontinuity plane, with a sense (when $\bar{p}$ is positive) that tends to dilate the discontinuity. When determining **r** it is necessary to consider the forces that act upon the block, as opposed to their reactions. This means that the water force associated with any discontinuity plane that *underlies* a given block must have an *upward* sense; the water force from a plane that *overlies* the block will have a *downward* sense. In most cases, simple inspection of the scaled plan view or the associated spherical triangle on the inclined hemisphere projection will reveal whether a given plane underlies or overlies a particular block. However, the following guidelines may be helpful when considering marginal cases (the words in parentheses are applicable in the case of a non-overhanging face):

If N_{hr} plots inside the spherical triangle and the face is overhanging (non-overhanging) then all planes overlie (underlie) the block. If N_{hr} plots outside the spherical triangle and the face is overhanging (non-overhanging), and it is possible to count an internal angle from N_{hr} along a great circle to any block surface line on a given plane without *crossing* the perimeter of the spherical triangle, then the given plane underlies (overlies) the associated block; otherwise it overlies (underlies) the block.

For example in Figure 7.7, which is an inclined hemisphere projection constructed for an overhanging face, planes 1, 2 and 4 all overlie block 1,2,4; however, plane 4 underlies and planes 1 and 5 overlie block 1,4,5. In Figure 8.9 which represents a non-overhanging face, plane 3 overlies and planes 1 and 2 underlie block 1,2,3. Any plane that passes through N_{hr} must be vertical. If such a plane applies water pressure to a given block then the associated force vector **h** will be horizontal. If the trend direction of this force is selected so that it lies on the same side of the vertical plane as the block, then the force can always be taken to have a positive sense. Discontinuity planes are rarely exactly vertical, so this complication seldom arises. If it does arise, however, it may be helpful to sketch a cross section through the block, in a horizontal plane, with the assistance of the associated scaled plan view, to remove any uncertainty concerning the appropriate trend direction.

The best way to determine the average water pressure $\bar{p}$ for a given discontinuity plane is to measure it directly, using suitable piezometers. Alternatively, if the boundary conditions controlling water flow are known, it may be possible to estimate $\bar{p}$ from some numerical or analytical model of water flow through the rock mass. One simple approach is to assume that the water pressure over a given block surface triangle varies linearly from zero on the perimeter of the triangle to some maximum value, p_{max}. This assumption, which implies that the pressure distribution is tetrahedral in shape, gives a mean pressure $\bar{p}$ equal to $p_{max}/3$. In some cases, particularly at non-overhanging rock slopes that have a subhorizontal top, it is possible to estimate a likely range of values for p_{max} by considering the location of the water table and the hydraulic properties of the discontinuities. It must be admitted, however, that in many stability calculations there is a high degree of uncertainty attached to the assumed values of water pressure. This problem is best tackled by investigating the sensitivity of the factor of safety to changing water pressures over some appropriate range of values.

It is now possible to summarise the complete process of analysing the stability of rigid blocks exposed at planar free faces:

(1) The relevant discontinuity characteristics, in particular orientation, frequency and size, are determined from measurements taken at exposed rock faces or from borehole core (Ch. 4).
(2) The discontinuity orientation data are analysed to determine any preferred orientations, or sets (Ch.5).
(3) An inclined hemisphere projection, containing all the relevant discontinuity sets, is constructed for the face under examination (Section 7.3).
(4) The geometrical properties of potentially unstable tetrahedral blocks are determined by constructing a scaled plan view of each block from the associated spherical triangle (Section 8.2).
(5) The resultant **r** of the various forces that act on each block is determined (Section 6.3) and the category of block behaviour is deduced (Section 7.4). Blocks in category I are assumed to be stable and those in category III are assumed to be unstable, whatever the magnitude of **r**.
(6) For blocks in category II, the shear strength parameters for those discontinuity planes that are deduced to be involved in sliding are determined from a suitable programme of field or laboratory tests. The resultant force **r** is decomposed to determine its normal and shear components on the plane(s) of sliding (Section 6.4). These components are then used, together with the appropriate shear strength parameters, to obtain the factor of safety of the block (Section 8.1).

Steps 5 and 6 of this process are best illustrated by means of simple examples. In these examples, and also the exercises at the end of the chapter, all forces are assumed to act through the centre of mass of the rigid body under analysis, thereby obviating the need to consider rotational instability and the associated equations of moment equilibrium. In order to minimise rounding errors and facilitate checking, intermediate results have been quoted to more significant figures than the precision of the graphical methods would normally justify.

Example 8.4 (Figs 8.5, 8.6 & 8.11) The block whose geometrical properties were analysed in Example 8.1 at a horizontal overhanging face has a unit weight of 25 kN/m^3. It is known that the three discontinuity planes that form the upper surfaces of the block each carry a mean water pressure of 10 kN/m^2. Determine the trend, plunge magnitude and sense of the additional force, **a**, that would, in theory, be required to maintain the block in static equilibrium.

The geometrical properties, calculated in Example 8.1, can be used to determine the forces involved in this example. The triangular faces of the block have areas $A_f = 10.07 \text{ m}^2$, $A_1 = 4.58 \text{ m}^2$, $A_2 = 7.71 \text{ m}^2$ and $A_3 = 3.35 \text{ m}^2$ while the block has a volume of 4.97 m^3. The magnitude of the vertical weight vector, **g**, which has a downward sense, is found from the product of unit weight and block volume, giving in this case a value of 124.2 kN. The water forces $\mathbf{h}_1$, $\mathbf{h}_2$ and $\mathbf{h}_3$ on the three discontinuity planes have magnitudes given by the products of mean water pressure and the areas of the planes involved, giving in this case values of 45.8, 77.1 and 33.5 kN respectively. These water forces each have a downward sense and act along lines that are normal to their respective discontinuity planes. These planes have dip directions/dip amounts (1) 138/51, (2) 355/40 and (3) 219/67, so their normals have trends/plunges (1) 318/39, (2) 175/50 and (3) 039/23. The resultant **r** of the four forces that act upon the block can now be found by applying the methods explained in Chapter 6. The resultant acts in a vertical direction, has a magnitude of approximately 225.2 kN and a downward sense.

The forces involved are summarised below and also plotted on the lower-hemisphere projection in Figure 8.11.

Force	Trend (deg)	Plunge (deg)	Magnitude (kN)	Sense
g	–	90	124.2	down
$\mathbf{h_1}$	318	39	45.8	down
$\mathbf{h_2}$	175	50	77.1	down
$\mathbf{h_3}$	039	23	33.5	down
r	–	90	225.2	down

Since, in this case, the rock face is horizontal and overhanging, the great circles of planes 1, 2 and 3 on the ordinary lower-hemisphere projection in Figure 8.11 intersect to give the kinematically congruent spherical triangle for the tetrahedral block. The vertical resultant force vector **r** plots at the centre of this projection, within the spherical triangle, indicating that the associated block is in category III and is free to move in the direction of **r**. The additional force, **a**, required to maintain static equilibrium must, therefore, act in a vertical direction, have a magnitude of 225.2 kN and act with an upward sense to balance the effect of **r**. This implies that a minimum support pressure of 22.3 kN/m² distributed over the face triangle would be required to keep the block in place. This support pressure could be provided by some suitable pattern of rock bolts.

The above example serves to illustrate a useful general principle concerning the effects of a single uniform normal pressure applied to three faces of a tetrahedron: the three forces generated by a uniform pressure $\bar{p}$ acting in a normal direction on any three faces of a tetrahedron are always in static equilibrium with a fourth force generated by the same uniform normal pressure acting on the fourth face of the tetrahedron. This is so because any body that is subjected only to pure hydrostatic pressure in this way must be in static equilibrium. In the above example, the resultant of $\mathbf{h_1}$, $\mathbf{h_2}$ and $\mathbf{h_3}$ acts in a vertical direction, with a magnitude of 101.0 kN and a downward sense. The fourth face of the tetrahedron is the face triangle, which in this case is horizontal and has an area A_f of approximately 10.07 m². The uniform pressure $\bar{p}$ of 10 kN/m² acting on

this face would, therefore, generate a force of 100.7 kN acting in a vertical direction with an upward sense. Allowing for the slight imprecision in the graphical construction this force would be in static equilibrium with $\mathbf{h_1}$, $\mathbf{h_2}$ and $\mathbf{h_3}$. In problems of this type, therefore, where a constant uniform pressure acts on three faces of a tetrahedron, it is usually easier to determine their resultant effect indirectly, by considering the effect of the same pressure on the fourth face and taking the reverse sense of the associated hypothetical force.

It is important to appreciate the distinction between the effects of an average uniform pressure $\bar{p}$ acting in a normal direction on the four faces of a tetrahedron and the effects of complete submergence of a solid tetrahedron of volume V in a fluid of unit weight γ_w. In the former case the body is in static equilibrium; in the latter case there is a vertical uplift or buoyancy force of magnitude $\gamma_w V$. This latter effect, generated by complete submergence, can easily be incorporated into a stability analysis by taking the submerged unit weight $(\gamma - \gamma_w)$ when calculating the weight of the block

Example 8.5 (Figs 8.7, 8.8, 8.12 & 8.13) The block whose geometrical properties were analysed in Example 8.2 at an overhanging face of dip direction/dip amount 120/50 has a unit weight of 27 kN/m³. It is known that if the average water pressure on planes 1 and 3 is $\bar{p}$ then that on plane 2 is $1.4\bar{p}$. The effective shear strength parameters for plane 2 are $c' = 25$ kN/m² and $\phi' = 30°$. Determine the category of block behaviour and hence the factor of safety when (a) $\bar{p} = 0$ and (b) $\bar{p} = 10$ kN/m².

The geometrical properties calculated in Example 8.2 can be used to determine the forces involved in this example. In this case the triangular faces of the block have areas $A_f = 24.77$ m², $A_1 = 23.52$ m², $A_2 = 9.27$ m² and $A_3 = 21.81$ m², while the block has a volume of 29.48 m³. The magnitude of the vertical weight vector, **g**, is again found from the product of unit weight and block volume, giving in this case a value of 796.0 kN. As always, this force has a downward sense.

(a) When $\bar{p} = 0$ the block is subject only to simple gravitational loading and the resultant force $\mathbf{r_a}$ acting on the block is given by the vertical weight vector **g**. In this case, from Example 8.2 and Figure 8.7, the block is deduced to be in category IIa and to slide, if unstable, along the line of maximum dip of plane 2 of dip direction/dip amount 325/32. In order to determine the stability of the block it is necessary to decompose the resultant force $\mathbf{r_a}$ to find its components normal to and parallel to the plane of potential sliding, using one of the methods in Chapter 6. The normal component **n** acts along a line of trend/plunge 145/58. The component **s** parallel to the plane must be coplanar with $\mathbf{r_a}$ and **n**. The magnitude $|\mathbf{s}|$ of this parallel component gives the maximum shearing

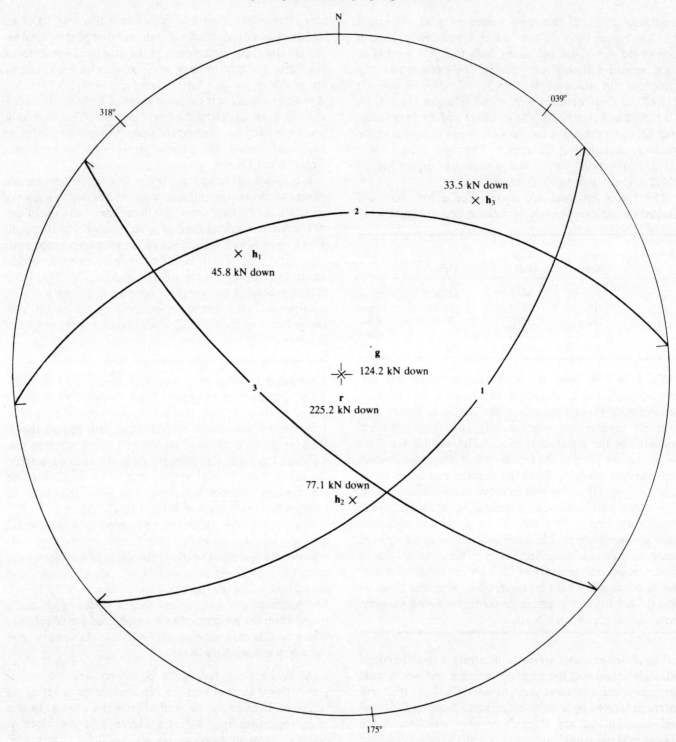

N

318°

039°

33.5 kN down
× **h₃**

2

× **h₁**
45.8 kN down

g
✳ 124.2 kN down

3   1

r
225.2 kN down

77.1 kN down
h₂ ×

175°

Figure 8.11   Resultant of four forces (Example 8.4).

force in the plane of sliding; its orientation and sense give the direction of sliding if the block is unstable. In this example r_a is vertical, so **s** must lie along the line of maximum dip of plane 2, of trend/plunge 325/32, at 90° to **n** as shown in Figure 8.12. In this particular case, since r_a is vertical and plots between **s** and **n**, it is possible to use Equations 6.14, identifying the vectors r_a, **s** and **n** with **r**,

u and **v** respectively, and the angle of dip of plane 2 with the angle β_u in these equations. Hence $|\mathbf{s}| = 796.0 \sin 32°$ = 421.8 kN and $|\mathbf{n}| = 796.0 \cos 32° = 675.0$ kN. Both of these forces have the same downward sense as r_a. Although there are no water pressures involved, it is necessary to know the area of the potential sliding plane so that its cohesive strength can be determined. This area of plane 2,

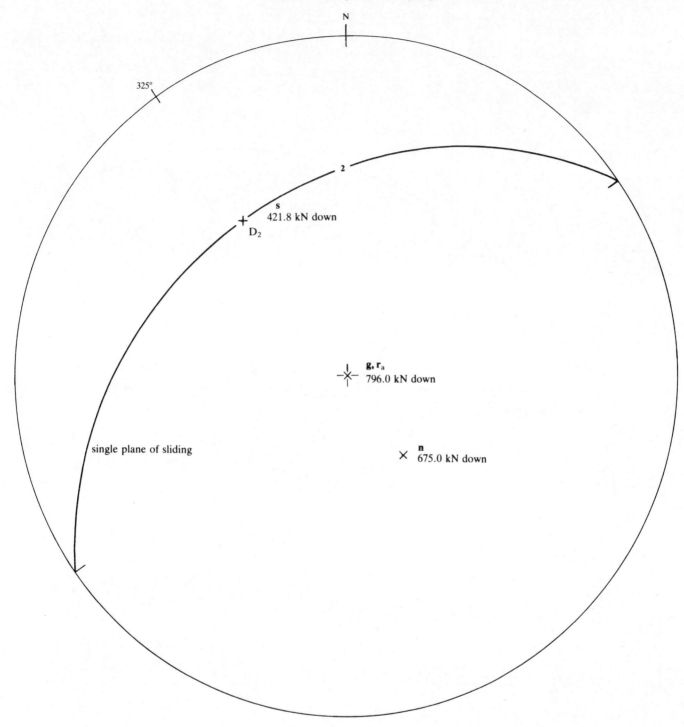

Figure 8.12 Forces acting on a single plane of sliding (Example 8.5a).

determined in Example 8.2, is 9.27 m². Equation 8.2 can now be used to determine the factor of safety of the block, giving in this case a value $F = 1.47$. This implies that, under dry conditions, the block is stable.

(b) When $\bar{p} = 10$ kN/m² there are additional forces affecting the block, generated by the average water pressures acting on the discontinuity planes bounding the block. The average pressure on planes 1 and 3 is 10 kN/m²; that on plane 2 is 14 kN/m². These pressures produce forces h_1, h_2 and h_3 acting normally to planes 1, 2 and 3 with magnitudes 235.2, 129.8 and 218.1 kN respectively. The force h_2 has an upward sense; the other two have a downward sense. The resultant r_b of these forces and the weight vector g can be found by applying the methods

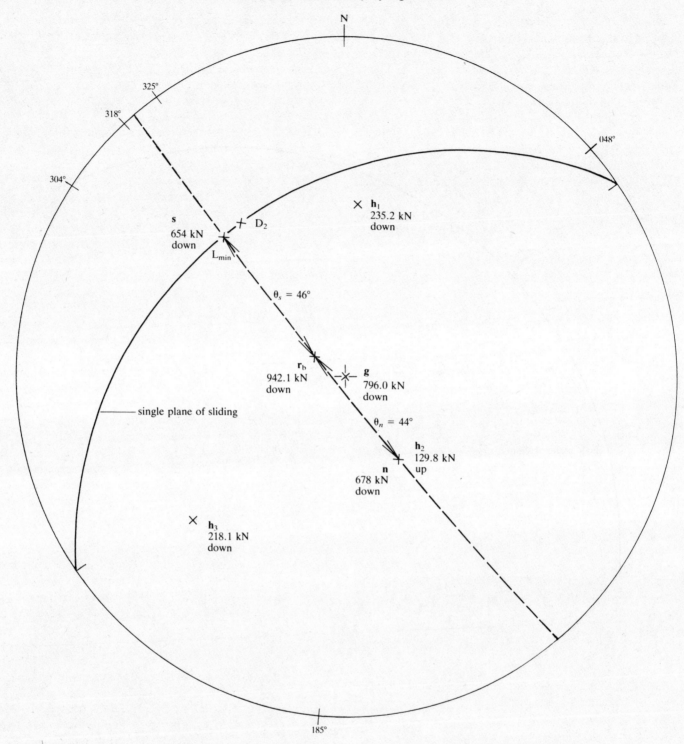

Figure 8.13 Forces acting on a single plane of sliding (Example 8.5b).

explained in Chapter 6. The various forces involved are summarised below and also plotted on the lower-hemisphere projection in Figure 8.13.

Force	Trend (deg)	Plunge (deg)	Magnitude (kN)	Sense
g	–	90	796.0	down
h_1	005	36	235.2	down
h_2	145	58	129.8	up
h_3	228	26	218.1	down
r_b	304.2	77.5	942.1	down

The resultant vector r_b has also been plotted as r_{br} on the inclined hemisphere projection in Figure 8.7. This shows that the block is still classified as category IIa and will, if unstable, slide along L_{min}, which in this case is a line in plane 2 defined by the intersection between this plane and the plane containing r_{br} and the normal to plane 2. The trend and plunge of L_{min}, measured from the lower-hemisphere projection in Figure 8.13, are approximately 318/32. It is now necessary to decompose r_b to find its components normal to and parallel to the plane of potential sliding. Again, the normal component acts along the normal to plane 2. However, since r_b is not vertical, the parallel component s does not act along the line of maximum dip of plane 2, but acts along L_{min} which is coplanar with r_b and n. As before, the magnitude $|s|$ of this parallel component gives the maximum shear force in the plane of potential sliding and its orientation and sense give the direction of sliding if the block is unstable. The forces n and s can be determined using the graphical method explained in Section 6.4 and the associated Equations 6.12 and 6.13. The vectors r_b, s and n are identified with r, u and v respectively, and the angles θ_s and θ_n in Figure 8.13 with θ_u and θ_v in these equations. In this case r_b plots between s and n, so these components must have the same downward sense as r_b. The angles θ_s and θ_n in Figure 8.13 are $46°$ and $44°$ respectively, which, when put in Equations 6.12 and 6.13, give $|s| \simeq 654$ kN and $|n| \simeq 678$ kN. Equation 8.2 can now be used to determine the factor of safety of the block, giving in this case a value $F = 0.95$. This implies that the block is marginally unstable and will slide along plane 2 in the direction given by L_{min}. The water pressures have not only reduced the stability of the block but have also 'pushed' the sliding direction away from the line of maximum dip of plane 2. In practice, the water pressures on planes 1 and 3 would probably drain away to zero as their apertures opened up during the early stages of block sliding. In this case a more realistic, but less conservative, model of block behaviour could be obtained by setting h_1 and h_3 to zero. Under these conditions, the block restabilises with a factor of safety of approximately 1.3.

Example 8.6 (Figs 8.9, 8.10, 8.14 & 8.15) The block whose geometrical properties were analysed in Example 8.3 at a non-overhanging face of dip direction/dip amount 163/58 has a unit weight of 26 kN/m^3. The effective shear strength parameters for planes 1 and 2 are $c_1' = 5$ kN/m^2, $\phi_1' = 26°$, $c_2' = 10$ kN/m^2 and $\phi_2' = 31°$. It is known that the maximum water pressure, p_{max}, on planes 1 and 2 occurs at the point m along the line of intersection, I_{12}, between these two planes, and that $p_{max} = \gamma_w z_w$, where γ_w is the unit weight of water and z_w is the vertical distance between m and the point where I_{12} intersects the top of the slope. Determine the category of block behaviour, and hence the factor of safety, when m occurs (a) at the top of the slope, (b) halfway along I_{12}, and (c) at the face of the rock slope. Assume that $\gamma_w = 9.8$ kN/m^3.

The geometrical properties calculated in Example 8.3 can be used to determine the forces involved in this example. The triangular faces of the block have areas $A_f = 34.26$ m^2, $A_1 = 36.30$ m^2, $A_2 = 46.35$ m^2 and $A_3 = 27.12$ m^2, while the block has a volume of 67.37 m^3. The line of intersection, I_{12}, between planes 1 and 2 has a true length given by $l_{12}/\cos\beta_{12} = 16.60$ m. Plane 3 is an additional non-overhanging free face that forms the top of the rock slope. The downward-acting vertical weight vector, g, has a magnitude of 1751.6 kN, given by the product of block volume and unit weight.

(a) When m occurs at the top of the slope, $z_w = 0$ and so there are no water pressures acting on the block. In this case the block is subject only to simple gravitational loading and the resultant force acting on the block is given by the vertical weight vector g. Referring to Example 8.3 and Figure 8.9, the block is deduced to be in category IIb and to slide, if unstable, along L_{max}, which is the line of intersection between planes 1 and 2, of trend/plunge 173/37, as shown on the lower-hemisphere projection in Figure 8.14. To determine the stability of the block it is necessary to decompose the resultant force r_a to find its components n_1 and n_2 normal to the two planes involved in sliding and also the component s parallel to their line of intersection, I_{12}. This can be done by using either the general vector method explained in Section 6.4 and Appendix B or the graphical method associated with Equations 6.12 and 6.13. When using the graphical method it is necessary to decompose the force in two stages, via an intermediate component t, as illustrated earlier in Example 6.10. In the first stage, r_a is decomposed to give the component s and the intermediate component t which is coplanar with r_a and s, and normal to s, as shown in Figure 8.14. Since r_a is vertical and plots between s and t it is possible to use Equations 6.14, identifying the vectors r_a, s and t with r, u and v respectively and the angle of plunge of I_{12} with the angle β_u in these equations. Hence $|s| = 1054.2$ kN and $|t| = 1398.9$ kN. Both of these forces have the same downward sense as r_a. It is now possible to decompose t further to give n_1 and n_2. This time it is necessary to use Equations 6.12 and 6.13, identifying the vectors t, n_1 and n_2 with r, u and v respectively and the angles θ_{n1} and θ_{n2} in Figure 8.14 with θ_u and θ_v in these equations. The vector t plots between n_1 and n_2, so these components must have the same downward sense as t. The angles θ_{n1} and θ_{n2} in Figure 8.14 are $59°$ and $36°$ respectively[2], which when put in Equations 6.12 and 6.13 give $|n_1| \simeq 825$ kN and $|n_2| \simeq 1204$ kN. The more general vector method gives $|s| = 1056.0$ kN, $|n_1| = 825.0$ kN and $|n_2| = 1214.4$ kN. Equation 8.3 can now be used to

---

[2] These angles need not, and in this case do not, add up to $90°$.

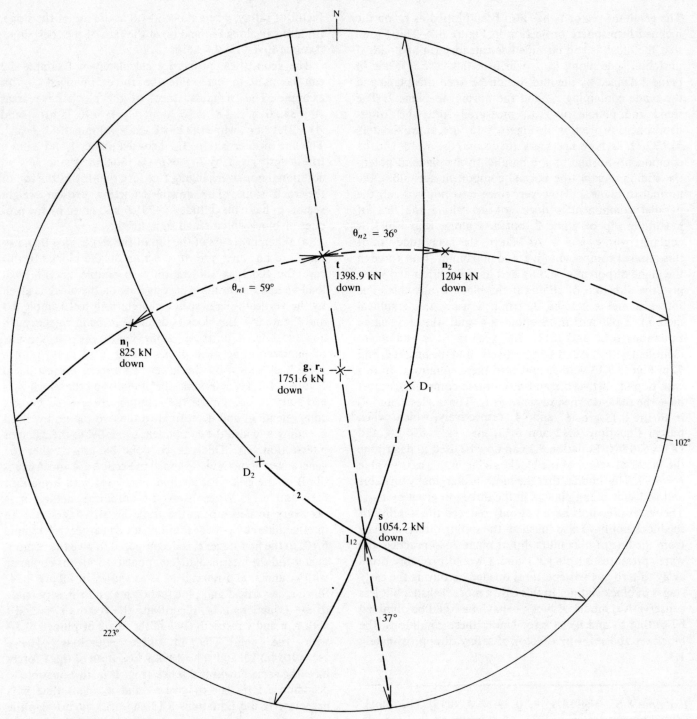

Figure 8.14 Forces acting on two planes of sliding (Example 8.6a).

determine the factor of safety of the block, giving a value $F = 1.68$, which represents a stable condition.

(b) In this second part, the maximum water pressure, p_{max} occurs halfway along I_{12}. This line of intersection has a true length of 16.60 m and an angle of plunge of $37°$. In this case, therefore, $z_w = 16.6 \sin 37°/2 = 5.0$ m, giving $p_{max} = 49.0$ kN/m². The approach used here is to assume

that water pressure varies linearly over planes 1 and 2 from p_{max} down to zero at the two free faces. The mean pressure, $\bar{p}$, on planes 1 and 2 is, therefore, $p_{max}/3 = 16.33$ kN/m². Plane 3, being a free face, is assumed to carry no excess pressure. The water forces $\mathbf{h}_1$ and $\mathbf{h}_2$ acting normally to planes 1 and 2 have magnitudes of 592.8 and 756.9 kN respectively. Both of these forces

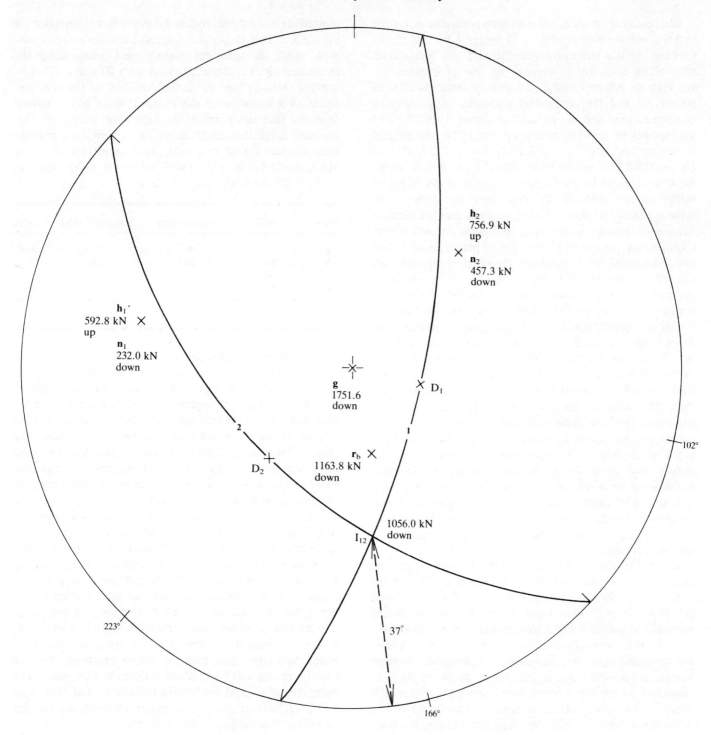

Figure 8.15 Forces acting on two planes of sliding (Example 8.6b).

have an upward sense. The resultant, r_b, of these forces and the weight vector g can be found by applying the methods in Chapter 6. The various forces involved are summarised below and also plotted on the lower-hemisphere projection in Figure 8.15.

Force	Trend (deg)	Plunge (deg)	Magnitude (kN)	Sense
g	–	90	1751.6	down
h_1	282	24	592.8	up
h_2	043	40	756.9	up
r_b	166.0	61.6	1163.8	down

The resultant vector $\mathbf{r}_b$ has also been plotted as $\mathbf{r}_{br}$ on the inclined hemisphere projection in Figure 8.9. This shows that the block is still in category IIb and will, if unstable, slide along L_{max} which is again the line of intersection, I_{12}, between planes 1 and 2. It is now necessary to decompose $\mathbf{r}_b$ to find the component $\mathbf{s}$ parallel to I_{12} and the components $\mathbf{n}_1$ and $\mathbf{n}_2$ normal to planes 1 and 2. The magnitudes of these components, found by the general vector method, are $|\mathbf{s}| = 1056.0$ kN, $|\mathbf{n}_1| = 232.0$ kN and $|\mathbf{n}_2| = 457.3$ kN, all of which have a downward sense. Equation 8.3 can be used again to determine the factor of safety of the block under these new conditions. The resulting factor of safety of 0.98 suggests that the block is marginally unstable under these conditions and will fail by sliding along the line of intersection of planes 1 and 2. The only additional forces acting on the block compared with the dry case considered previously are $\mathbf{h}_1$ and $\mathbf{h}_2$, which act normally to planes 1 and 2. Since the magnitudes of these are both less than the *dry* values for $|\mathbf{n}_1|$ and $|\mathbf{n}_2|$ respectively, it is quite permissible to determine the new normal forces under wet conditions simply by subtracting $|\mathbf{h}_1|$ and $|\mathbf{h}_2|$ from these dry values. The magnitude of $\mathbf{s}$ is the same in both the dry and wet cases. If, however, the original normal force on a given plane under dry conditions is less than the dilatant normal force generated by water pressures, then the plane will tend to open up under wet conditions, leading to a different sliding mechanism if the block is unstable. This will necessitate a reanalysis of the normal and shear forces on the plane(s) that is (are) deduced to be involved in sliding. This effect is always automatically catered for when the category of block behaviour is deduced from the orientation of the resultant force, acting on the block, relative to the associated spherical triangle, as explained in Section 7.4.

(c) In this final part, the maximum water pressure, p_{max}, occurs at the face of the rock slope. This means that $z_w = 9.99$ m, giving $p_{max} = 97.9$ kN/m^2 and $\bar{p} = 32.63$ kN/m^2. The water forces $\mathbf{h}_1$ and $\mathbf{h}_2$ acting normally to planes 1 and 2 have magnitudes of 1184.5 and 1512.4 kN respectively, both with an upward sense. Allowing for rounding errors, the values of z_w, and also the water forces, are double those in part (b) of this example. The resultant, $\mathbf{r}_c$, of these forces and the weight vector $\mathbf{g}$ is found in the usual way. The various forces involved are summarised below, while the resultant vector $\mathbf{r}_c$ has been

plotted as $\mathbf{r}_{cr}$ on the inclined hemisphere projection in Figure 8.9. This shows that the resultant force vector now plots inside the spherical triangle, and consequently the associated block is classified as category III and will fail by moving through free air in the direction of the resultant force. In practical terms this means that the block 'bursts' from the face as a result of the high water pressures. This extreme condition could never be achieved in practice because part (b) of this example demonstrates that the block would fail by sliding well before the water pressures could build up to the required level.

Force	Trend (deg)	Plunge (deg)	Magnitude (kN)	Sense
$\mathbf{g}$	–	90	1751.6	down
$\mathbf{h}_1$	282	24	1184.5	up
$\mathbf{h}_2$	043	40	1512.4	up
$\mathbf{r}_c$	166.0	15.1	1144.7	down

There are two important principles illustrated in these examples and also the exercises at the end of this chapter. The first is that for a given block geometry the mode of failure is critically dependent upon the orientation of the resultant force that acts upon the block. Indeed a small change in the orientation of this force can change the plane(s) involved in sliding. The second principle is that the behaviour and stability of a given block can be highly sensitive to changes in the assumed values of water pressure on the planes bounding the block.

The reader should now be in a position to analyse, by graphical methods, the stability of any tetrahedral block, exposed at an overhanging or non-overhanging face of any orientation, and subject to any combination of external forces and water pressures. It is hoped that these graphical methods have provided not only an introduction to the principles involved but also a valuable tool for the design and analysis of engineering structures in rock. Ultimately, however, it may be preferable to use computer programs, based upon the principles of vector methods, for the routine analysis of rigid block failures at free faces. The comprehensive texts by Warburton (1981) and Goodman and Shi (1984) are recommended to those readers who wish to pursue this subject in more depth.

Exercises

8.1 An overhanging planar rock face of dip direction/dip amount 125/30 has a length of 80 m measured along its strike and a width x measured along its line of maximum dip. It is known that the rock face is intersected by three extensive planar discontinuity sets of dip direction/dip amount (1) 189/66, (2) 346/45 and (3) 110/68, each of which is subjected to an average water pressure $\bar{p}$. The unit weight of the rock material is 28 kN/m^3 (i) Determine the geometrical properties of the largest tetrahedral block that could fall from the rock face under simple gravitational loading when (a) $x = 7$ m and (b) $x = 11$ m. (ii) Determine the minimum additional force that must be applied to the largest tetrahedral block to maintain it in static equilibrium when (a) $x = 7$ m, $\bar{p} = 0$, (b) $x = 7$ m, $\bar{p} = 10$ kN/m^2, (c) $x = 11$ m, $\bar{p} = 0$ and (d) $x = 11$ m, $\bar{p} = 10$ kN/m^2.

8.2 A horizontal, overhanging planar rock face of rectangular shape measures 10 m by 20 m, with its longer dimension at an azimuth 090°. The face is intersected by three extensive planar discontinuity sets of dip direction/dip amount (1) 290/40, (2) 014/76 and (3) 310/20. Determine the volume of the largest tetrahedral block that could slide from the rock face under simple gravitational loading. The effective shear strength parameters for discontinuities from sets 1 and 2 are $c_1' = 10$ kN/m^2, $\phi_1' = 35°$ and $c_2' = 15$ kN/m^2, $\phi_2' = 30°$ respectively. The unit weight of the rock material is 26 kN/m^3. It is known that the average water pressure on discontinuities from sets 1 and 2 is $\bar{p}$ while that on set 3 is always zero. Determine the potential sliding direction, the plane(s) involved in sliding and also the factor of safety of the largest block when (i) $\bar{p} = 0$ and (ii) $\bar{p} = 12$ kN/m^2.

8.3 A non-overhanging planar rock slope of dip direction/dip amount 140/52, with a horizontal top, is intersected by two planar discontinuities to form a kinematically feasible tetrahedral wedge. The geometrical and shear strength properties of the two discontinuity planes forming the wedge are as follows:

Discontinuity	Dip direction/ dip amount	Area (m^2)	c' (kN/m^2)	ϕ' (deg)
1	196/40	60.0	6.0	35
2	093/60	50.0	10.0	30

The associated block has a volume of 105.0 m^3 and a unit weight of 25 kN/m^3. Determine the factor of safety of the wedge against double plane sliding failure when (i) the slope is dry, and (ii) the mean water pressure on both discontinuity planes is 8 kN/m^2.

8.4 A non-overhanging planar rock slope of dip direction/dip amount 030/60 has a planar top of dip direction/dip amount 025/10. Two planar discontinuities intersect each other, the top and the face of the rock slope to form a potentially unstable tetrahedral block. The orientations and shear strength parameters for the two discontinuity planes are as follows:

Discontinuity	Dip direction/dip amount	c' (kN/m^2)	ϕ' (deg)
1	335/51	20	25
2	067/65	10	32

It is observed that the side of the face triangle formed by plane 1 has a length of 20 m. The rock material has a unit weight of 25 kN/m^3. Determine the factor of safety of the block against sliding failure and also the plane(s) involved in sliding when (i) the slope is dry and (ii) after torrential rain, when the peak water pressure beneath the block occurs a quarter of the way down the line of intersection between planes 1 and 2.

Answers to these exercises are given on page 123.

Appendix

A Projection of areas

A.1 Equal-angle projection of a small circle

Figure A.1 shows a three-dimensional view of a reference sphere, referred to in Chapter 2, which contains a small circle centred on point P′ on the lower reference hemisphere. The aim here is to demonstrate that the equal-angle projection of this small circle is itself circular in shape. The proof given here is based partly upon work by Phillips (1963).

The locus of points on the perimeter of the small circle in Figure A.1 is projected along straight lines, drawn from the top point, T, of the reference sphere, to generate the equal-angle projection of the small circle. These lines together form a conical shape centred on the axis TP′. The plane, S, containing the small circle on the perimeter of the reference sphere produces, by definition, a circular cross section through this cone. This plane is not, however, in general, normal to the axis TP′. Consequently, any section through the cone, taken normal to the axis TP′ must be elliptical in shape, with its minor axis in the plane OTP′ and a horizontal major axis. If such a normal plane were rotated about this major axis until it became parallel to the plane S, the elliptical cross-section would become circular. By symmetry, a circular cross section would also be obtained by rotating the plane about the major axis of the normal section but in the opposite direction. The resulting conjugate section would be inclined at the same angle to the axis TP′ as plane S. The following proof seeks to demonstrate that the horizontal plane of projection is conjugate with plane S, and therefore generates a circular section through the conical locus.

Figure A.2 shows a vertical section through the centre, O, of the reference sphere and through the centre of the small circle generated by an apex angle δ, as previously illustrated in Figure 2.3. The centre of this small circle is represented by the point P′ on the surface of the lower reference hemisphere, which projects to give the point P on the horizontal plane of projection. Two points, P_1' and P_2', on the perimeter of the small circle in the plane of the section project to give points P_1 and P_2 on the plane of projection. The line JP_2' in Figure A.2 is constructed so that it is parallel to the line HP_2, the latter lying in the plane of projection. A second line LP_2' in this figure is constructed normal to the axis TP′.

By symmetry

$$TJ = TP_2'$$

hence

$$T\hat{J}P_2' = T\hat{P}_2'J$$

but

$$T\hat{J}P_2' = T\hat{P}_1'P_2' \quad \text{(angles on equal arcs)}$$

therefore

$$T\hat{P}_2'J = T\hat{P}_1'P_2'$$

i.e.

$$T\hat{P}_2'K = L\hat{P}_1'P_2' \tag{A.1}$$

Now

$$T\hat{L}P_2' = T\hat{P}_2'L \quad \text{(isoceles triangles)}$$

but

$$T\hat{L}P_2' = L\hat{P}_1'P_2' + L\hat{P}_2'P_1'$$
$$\text{(external angle of a triangle)} \tag{A.2}$$

and

$$T\hat{P}_2'L = T\hat{P}_2'K + K\hat{P}_2'L \tag{A.3}$$

Hence, combining Equations A.1, A.2 and A.3

$$L\hat{P}_2'P_1' = K\hat{P}_2'L$$

Consequently the section KP_2' is conjugate with the section $P_1'P_2'$ and must, therefore, generate a circular section through the cone. The section P_1P_2, being parallel to KP_2' must also generate a circular section. This proves that the equal-angle projection of a small circle is itself circular.

A.2 Equal-area projection of a small element of area

An important property of the equal-area projection is that the area enclosed by the small circle generated by a given cone angle δ about an axis of trend α and plunge β is constant for all values of α and β. It is the aim now to verify this property by considering a very small element of area $\Delta A'$ on the surface of the lower reference hemisphere and its equal-area projection, of area ΔA as shown in Figure A.3a. This proof is based partly upon that given by Attewell and Farmer (1976).

For the purposes of the following proof, the inclination of a given line will be expressed in terms of the angle φ that it makes with the vertical. Hence, for a line of plunge β,

$$\phi = \frac{\pi}{2} - \beta \tag{A.4}$$

where these and all other angles in this section of the appendix are in radians.

The element of area $\Delta A'$ on the surface of the lower reference hemisphere, of radius R, can be approximated by a small rectangular shape associated with a small increment, $\Delta\alpha$, of trend and a small increment, $\Delta\phi$, of inclination centred on a line of trend α and inclination φ. Figure A.3a shows that the increment of trend $\Delta\alpha$ produces a triangular-shaped segment on the surface of the hemisphere.

A small element of area cut out of this segment will have

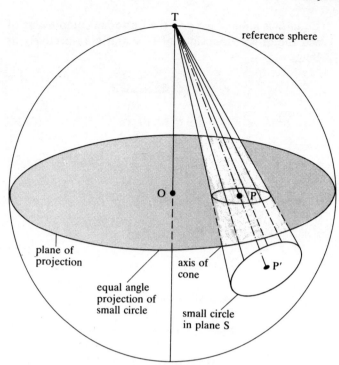

Figure A.1 Equal-angle projection of a small circle.

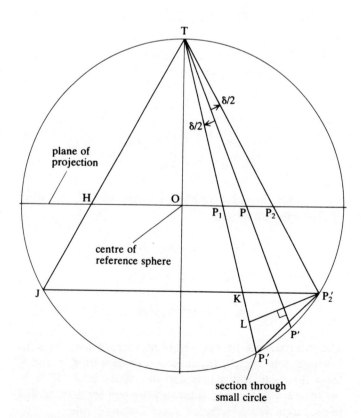

Figure A.2 Vertical section through the centre of the reference sphere, illustrating equal-angle projection of a small circle.

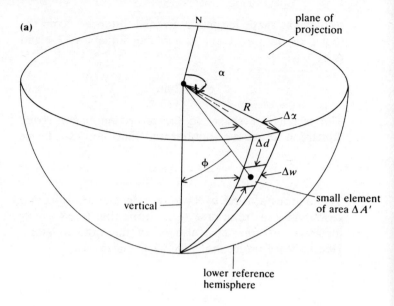

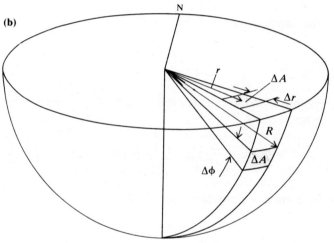

Figure A.3 Equal-area projection of a small element of area.

a width, Δw that depends upon the angle of inclination ϕ as follows

$$\Delta w = R\Delta\alpha \sin\phi \qquad (A.5)$$

The other dimension, Δd, of this element depends upon the increment of inclination $\Delta\phi$ in Figure A.3b as follows

$$\Delta d = R\Delta\phi \qquad (A.6)$$

Hence

$$\Delta A' = \Delta w \Delta d$$

or

$$\Delta A' = R^2 \sin\phi\, \Delta\alpha\Delta\phi \qquad (A.7)$$

The element of area $\Delta A'$ projects to give an area ΔA, which, when $\Delta A'$ is very small, can be approximated by a rectangular shape located at a radial distance r from the centre of the projection. Combining Equations 2.4 and A.4

$$r = R\sqrt{2}\sin\frac{\phi}{2} \qquad \text{(A.8)}$$

The rectangular shape on the projection has a radial dimension Δr and a circumferential dimension $r\Delta\alpha$, hence

$$\Delta A = r\Delta\alpha\Delta r \qquad \text{(A.9)}$$

The total surface area of the lower reference hemisphere is $2\pi R^2$ while the total area of its projection is πR^2. Any increment of area must also reflect this ratio of areas. Hence, if the projection is truly equal-area then

$$\frac{\Delta A'}{\Delta A} = \frac{2\pi R^2}{\pi R^2} = 2 \qquad \text{(A.10)}$$

Dividing Equation A.7 by A.9 gives

$$\frac{\Delta A'}{\Delta A} = \frac{R^2\sin\phi\,\Delta\phi}{r\Delta r} \qquad \text{(A.11)}$$

When $\Delta\phi$ and Δr are very small, writing down the general integrals gives

$$\frac{\Delta A'}{\Delta A} = \frac{R^2\int\sin\phi\,\mathrm{d}\phi}{\int r\,\mathrm{d}r} \qquad \text{(A.12)}$$

Differentiating Equation A.8 gives

$$\mathrm{d}r = \frac{R}{\sqrt{2}}\cos\frac{\phi}{2}\,\mathrm{d}\phi$$

which, when substituted into Equation A.12 together with the expression for r in Equation A.8, gives

$$\frac{\Delta A'}{\Delta A} = \frac{R^2\int\sin\phi\,\mathrm{d}\phi}{\int R\sqrt{2}\sin(\phi/2)(R/\sqrt{2})\cos(\phi/2)\,\mathrm{d}\phi} = 2 \qquad \text{(A.13)}$$

Comparison between Equations A.10 and A.13 confirms that the projection generated by Equation 2.4 is truly equal-area.

B Decomposition of a force

A known force $\mathbf{r}$ of trend α_r, plunge β_r, non-zero magnitude $|\mathbf{r}|$ and sense S_r is to be decomposed into three non-coplanar, non-parallel component forces $\mathbf{u}$, $\mathbf{v}$ and $\mathbf{w}$ subject to the requirement that their trends and plunges are respectively α_u, β_u, α_v, β_v, α_w and β_w. The aim is to find the unknown senses S_u, S_v, S_w and magnitudes $|\mathbf{u}|$, $|\mathbf{v}|$, $|\mathbf{w}|$ of the component vectors $\mathbf{u}$, $\mathbf{v}$ and $\mathbf{w}$ respectively.

Equations 6.4 and 6.5 give the Cartesian components of $\mathbf{r}$ and the direction cosines of $\mathbf{u}$, $\mathbf{v}$ and $\mathbf{w}$ respectively as follows

$$r_x = S_r\,|\mathbf{r}|\sin\alpha_r\cos\beta_r$$

$$r_y = S_r\,|\mathbf{r}|\cos\alpha_r\cos\beta_r \qquad \text{(A.14)}$$

$$r_z = S_r\,|\mathbf{r}|\sin\beta_r$$

$$l_x = \sin\alpha_u\cos\beta_u$$

$$l_y = \cos\alpha_u\cos\beta_u$$

$$l_z = \sin\beta_u$$

$$m_x = \sin\alpha_v\cos\beta_v$$

$$m_y = \cos\alpha_v\cos\beta_v \qquad \text{(A.15)}$$

$$m_z = \sin\beta_v$$

$$n_x = \sin\alpha_w\cos\beta_w$$

$$n_y = \cos\alpha_w\cos\beta_w$$

$$n_z = \sin\beta_w$$

The unknown senses and magnitudes of the component forces are represented as follows

$$U = S_u\,|\mathbf{u}|$$

$$V = S_v\,|\mathbf{v}| \qquad \text{(A.16)}$$

$$W = S_w\,|\mathbf{w}|$$

These form the three unknown values in the following simultaneous equations

$$r_x = Ul_x + Vm_x + Wn_x$$

$$r_y = Ul_y + Vm_y + Wn_y \qquad \text{(A.17)}$$

$$r_z = Ul_z + Vm_z + Wn_z$$

The components of the resultant force $\mathbf{r}$ form the inhomogeneous vector, the direction cosines of $\mathbf{u}$, $\mathbf{v}$ and $\mathbf{w}$ form the coefficient matrix and the values U, V, W form the solution vector. The following method for determining the solution vector is based upon Cramer's rule.

The first step is to evaluate the determinant $|A|$ of the coefficient matrix, as follows:

$$|A| = l_x(m_y n_z - m_z n_y) + m_x(l_z n_y - l_y n_z) + n_x(l_y m_z - l_z m_y)$$

$$(A.18)$$

If $|A|$ is equal to zero the problem is indeterminate. This occurs either when $\mathbf{u}$, $\mathbf{v}$ and $\mathbf{w}$ are all coplanar, or when two or more of these vectors are parallel to each other. It is important to remember that a force can only be decomposed into up to three non-coplanar non-parallel components.

Assuming that $|A|$ is non-zero, the next step is to evaluate the determinants of modified coefficient matrices as follows:

$$|A_1| = r_x(m_y n_z - m_z n_y) + m_x(r_z n_y - r_y n_z) + n_x(r_y m_z - r_z m_y)$$

$$|A_2| = l_x(r_y n_z - r_z n_y) + r_x(l_z n_y - l_y n_z) + n_x(l_y r_z - l_z r_y)$$

$$|A_3| = l_x(m_y r_z - m_z r_y) + m_x(l_z r_y - l_y r_z) + r_x(l_y m_z - l_z m_y)$$

$$(A.19)$$

Finally

$$U = |A_1|/|A|$$

$$V = |A_2|/|A| \qquad (A.20)$$

$$W = |A_3|/|A|$$

The signs of U, V and W give the senses of the forces $\mathbf{u}$, $\mathbf{v}$ and $\mathbf{w}$ respectively, a positive sign indicating a downward sense and a negative sign an upward sense. The absolute values of U, V and W give the magnitudes $|\mathbf{u}|$, $|\mathbf{v}|$ and $|\mathbf{w}|$ of the component forces.

C Computer generation of inclined hemisphere projections

C.1 Introduction

The construction of an inclined hemisphere projection, explained in Chapter 7, can be fairly time-consuming – particularly where there is a large number of discontinuity sets involved or where the angle of rotation is large. The effort is justified, however, by the relative ease with which the block geometry and also the category of block behaviour can be determined from the resulting projection. Recent developments in microcomputers have now made it possible to generate relatively complex diagrams, such as inclined hemisphere projections, in hard-copy form by means of simple graphics commands. The use of a computer for this work greatly reduces the time and effort required to produce each projection, thereby making it feasible to investigate a number of rock face orientations. It is the aim here to set out the theory underlying the construction of lower-hemisphere and inclined hemisphere projections to provide a basis for the development of

suitable computer programs in any appropriate language. The definitions and notation given in Section 1.2 and used in Chapter 7 will be employed throughout. The theory explained in this appendix is based upon that previously published by Priest (1983).

C.2 Lower-hemisphere projection

Figure A.4 shows the construction of a lower-hemisphere, equal-angle projection of radius R. The projection in this figure is made onto the xy plane of a left-handed Cartesian co-ordinate system in which x is horizontal to the east

(a) Plane of projection

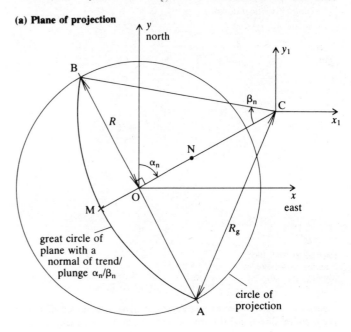

(b) Section

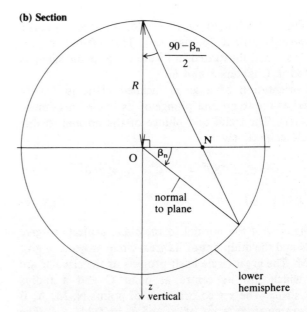

Figure A.4 Lower-hemisphere equal-angle projection of radius R. (a) plane of projection and (b) section normal to the plane of projection, through ON.

(a)

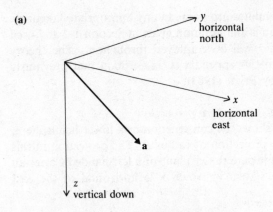

(b)

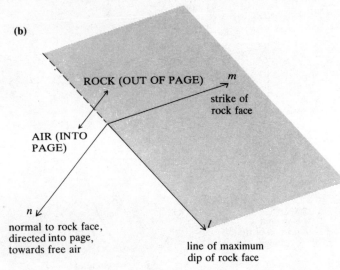

Figure A.5 Cartesian co-ordinate systems: (a) axes orientated relative to geographical directions; (b) axes orientated relative to the rock face.

(trend 090°), y is horizontal to the north (trend 0°) and z is downwards vertical (plunge 90°). This left-handed co-ordinate system, illustrated in Figure A.5a, is the same as that used in Chapters 5 and 6.

The orientation of a given inclined plane is usually recorded as the trend and plunge of its line of maximum dip (α_d,β_d). The trend and plunge of the normal to this plane are respectively

$$\alpha_n = \alpha_d \pm 180° \qquad 0° \leqslant \alpha_n \leqslant 360° \qquad \text{(A.21)}$$

$$\beta_n = 90° - \beta_d \qquad \text{(A.22)}$$

In Figure A.4 the normal to the plane projects to give point N and the midpoint of its great circle projects to give point M. The great circle itself projects as the circular arc AMB which has its centre at point C and a radius $R_g = R/\sin\beta_n$. The x,y co-ordinates of points N, M, A, B and C are given in terms of α_n and β_n in Table A.1. The value of R_g, and also the x,y co-ordinates of point C, become infinitely large as β_n approaches 0°. The simplest

Table A.1 The x,y, co-ordinates of points on a lower-hemisphere equal-angle projection of radius R.

Point	x	y
N	$R\sin\alpha_n\tan\left(45 - \dfrac{\beta_n}{2}\right)$	$R\cos\alpha_n\tan\left(45 - \dfrac{\beta_n}{2}\right)$
M	$-R\sin\alpha_n\tan\left(\dfrac{\beta_n}{2}\right)$	$-R\cos\alpha_n\tan\left(\dfrac{\beta_n}{2}\right)$
A	$R\cos\alpha_n$	$-R\sin\alpha_n$
B	$-R\cos\alpha_n$	$R\sin\alpha_n$
C	$R\sin\alpha_n\tan(90-\beta_n)$	$R\cos\alpha_n\tan(90-\beta_n)$

way to avoid this difficulty is to set temporarily the minimum value of β_n to some small value, say 0.001°, during calculation of the x,y co-ordinates. On a lower-hemisphere projection the point M represents the line of maximum dip of the given plane; this is not the case on an inclined hemisphere projection.

The data given in Table A.1 can be used to construct lower-hemisphere equal-angle projections of the normals, lines of maximum dip and great circles of planes of any orientation. The perimeter of the circle of projection can be plotted by incrementing the trend value α in the range 0 to 360°, to generate a locus of points with x,y co-ordinates of $R\sin\alpha$ and $R\cos\alpha$ respectively. A similar approach is used to plot each great circle. In this case it is necessary to set up an auxiliary set of axes x_1,y_1, parallel to the first set but with its origin at point C. The great circle is then constructed by swinging the radius R_g in suitably small angular increments from A to B, as shown in Figure A.4a. This gives the x_1, y_1 co-ordinates, and hence the x,y co-ordinates, of the locus of points defining the great circle.

C.3 Inclined hemisphere projection
The orientation of any line of trend α and plunge β can be represented by a unit vector **a** constructed so that it is parallel to the given line. The components or direction cosines of this unit vector, relative to the Cartesian axes in Figure A.5a, are

$$a_x = \sin\alpha\cos\beta$$

$$a_y = \cos\alpha\cos\beta \qquad \text{(A.23)}$$

$$a_z = \sin\beta$$

Figure A.5b shows a second left-handed Cartesian co-ordinate system in which l is the line of maximum dip of the rock face, m is its strike and n its normal, with the direction of positive n pointing outwards, towards free air. The process of constructing an inclined hemisphere projection is exactly equivalent to producing a hemispherical projection onto the l,m plane, instead of the x,y plane, with the hemisphere of projection on the positive *n* side of the *l*,*m* plane. Figure 7.5 provides a diagrammatic illustration of this principle.

If the line of maximum dip of the rock face has a trend α_{df} and plunge β_{df} then the direction cosines of the *l*, *m*, *n* axes in the *x*, *y*, *z* system are as follows

$$l_x = S \sin \alpha_{df} \cos \beta_{df}$$

$$l_y = S \cos \alpha_{df} \cos \beta_{df}$$

$$l_z = S \sin \beta_{df}$$

$$m_x = - \cos \alpha_{df}$$

$$m_y = \sin \alpha_{df} \qquad (A.24)$$

$$m_z = 0$$

$$n_x = - S \sin \alpha_{df} \sin \beta_{df}$$

$$n_y = - S \cos \alpha_{df} \sin \beta_{df}$$

$$n_z = S \cos \beta_{df}$$

The parameter *S* is +1.0 for an overhanging face and −1.0 for a non-overhanging face. This parameter ensures that positive *n* is always directed outwards towards free air by, in effect, rotating the *l*, *m*, *n* system through 180° about the *m* axis if the face is non-overhanging. The components of the unit vector **a** relative to the *l*, *m*, *n* system are given by

$$a_l = T(l_x a_x + l_y a_y + l_z a_z)$$

$$a_m = T(m_x a_x + m_y a_y + m_z a_z) \qquad (A.25)$$

$$a_n = T(n_x a_x + n_y a_y + n_z a_z)$$

where the parameter *T* is chosen to be +1.0 or −1.0 so that $a_n \geqslant 0$. This parameter ensures that **a** is directed outwards towards free air, thereby intersecting the hemisphere of projection.

The next and most important step in the analysis is to calculate the apparent trend α' and the apparent plunge β' of **a** relative to the axes *l*, *m*, *n* which, for the purposes of defining trend and plunge, are taken to be equivalent to the *x*, *y*, *z* axes respectively. Applying Equations 5.12 and 5.13 gives

$$\alpha' = \arctan(a_l/a_m) + q \qquad (A.26)$$

$$\beta' = \arctan \left[a_n / \sqrt{(a_l^2 + a_m^2)} \right] \qquad (A.27)$$

As before, the parameter *q* is an angle that ensures that

α' lies in the correct quadrant and in the range 0–360°. This parameter is necessary because the arctangent function of most computers returns a value in the range −90° to +90°:

$$\text{if } a_l \geqslant 0 \text{ and } a_m \geqslant 0 \text{ then } q = 0°$$

$$\text{if } a_l < 0 \text{ and } a_m \geqslant 0 \text{ then } q = 360°$$

$$\text{for all other signs of } a_l \text{ and } a_m, \, q = 180°$$

Particular care must be taken to test whether the denominators in Equations A.26 and A.27 are equal to zero. If this occurs in Equation A.26 then α' is 90° if $a_l > 0$ and is 270° if $a_l < 0$; a zero denominator in Equation A.27 implies that $\beta' = 90°$.

For convenience, the north direction ($\alpha = 0°$) is usually labelled 'N' on a conventional lower-hemisphere projection. This reference direction is retained as the '12 o'clock' position on any resulting inclined hemisphere projection. The value of apparent trend α'_r relative to this direction is given by

$$\alpha'_r = \alpha' + \alpha_{df} - 90° \qquad (A.28)$$

An inclined hemisphere projection is most easily constructed by rotating the normals to the various planes involved. In this case the unit vector **a** may be regarded as the normal to the *i*th discontinuity plane of dip direction/dip amount α_{di}/β_{di}. The trend and plunge, α_{ni} and β_{ni}, of the normal to this plane are found using Equations A.21 and A.22 and then identified with α and β in Equation A.23 to determine the components of the normal unit vector **a**. The vector analysis, summarised in Equations A.24 to A.28, can be used to calculate the apparent trend α'_r, relative to the original 'N' direction, and the apparent plunge β' of the normal on an inclined hemisphere projection for a given face of dip direction/dip amount α_{df}/β_{df}. The expressions in Table A.1 can then be used to construct the equal-angle projections of the normal and the great circle of this *i*th plane by identifying the angles α'_r and β' with α_n and β_n respectively in this table. The midpoint of the great circle (point M in Figure A.4a) has no special significance on an inclined hemisphere projection and need not be plotted. The line of maximum dip of the *i*th plane does not plot at the midpoint of its great circle on an inclined hemisphere projection. In order to plot the rotated line of maximum dip, therefore, it is necessary to carry out a separate rotation for this line. To achieve this rotation, each line of maximum dip is, for convenience, treated in a similar way to a normal, this time identifying α_{di} and β_{di} with α and β in Equation A.23 to determine the components of the unit vector **a**. Again, the vector analysis in Equations A.24 to A.28 can be used to calculate the apparent trend α'_r and the apparent plunge β'

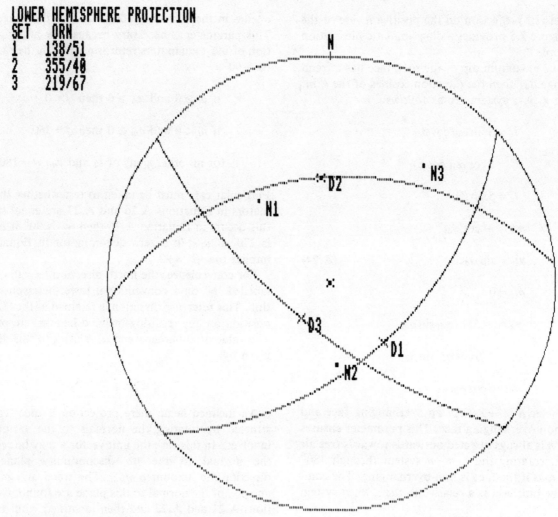

```
LOWER HEMISPHERE PROJECTION
SET  ORN
 1   138/51
 2   355/40
 3   219/67
```

Figure A.6 Computer-generated lower-hemisphere projection.

of the line of maximum dip on the inclined hemisphere projection for the given face of dip direction/dip amount α_{df}/β_{df}. The angles α_r' and β' calculated in this way are identified with α_n and β_n respectively in Table A.1 to give the x,y co-ordinates of point N on the inclined hemisphere projection. This point, which *in this case* represents the rotated line of maximum dip of the plane, will lie on the great circle of the plane in question. The other points, M, A, B and C, are, of course, ignored in this case.

The horizontal plane and its normal (the vertical direction) can be treated in the same way as the discontinuity planes, bearing in mind that the line of maximum dip of a horizontal plane is not defined and is not, therefore, plotted. The downward-directed end of the line of maximum dip of the rock face plots on the perimeter of the inclined hemisphere projection at an azimuth, relative to the *initial* north (N) direction, given by

$$\alpha_r' = \alpha_{df} \qquad \text{for an overhanging face}$$

$$\text{(A.29)}$$

$$\alpha_r' = \alpha_{df} \pm 180° \quad \text{for a non-overhanging face}$$

C.4 Computer-generated projections

The theory explained in the previous sections was implemented in a program 'IHP' written in BBC Basic for a Model B, BBC Microcomputer[1]. Either lower- or inclined hemisphere projections can be generated on the monitor screen, using Mode 0 high-resolution graphics. The program contains a procedure designed to dump the screen contents onto paper using a bit-addressable dot-matrix printer. Projections that are to be dumped to hard copy are automatically predistorted in the x direction to compensate for the x-axis distortion of the dot matrix. The following notation is used on the projections:

(a) Lower-hemisphere projection

       N   north point

[1] This is a 32 kbyte, high-resolution graphics microcomputer, commissioned by the British Broadcasting Corporation as part of their computer literacy project, and manufactured by Acorn Computers Ltd.

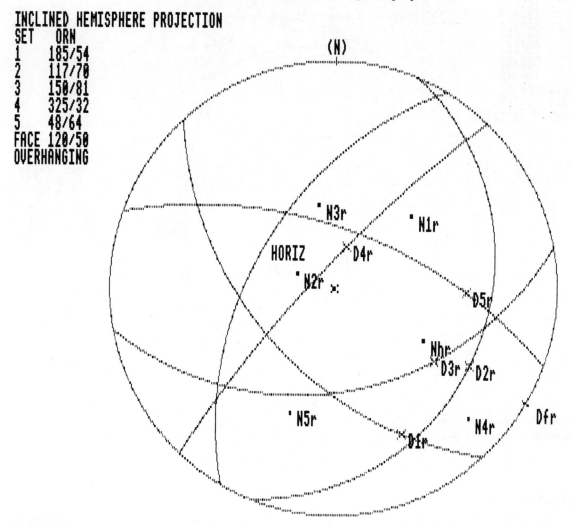

```
INCLINED HEMISPHERE PROJECTION
SET   ORN
1     185/54
2     117/70
3     150/81
4     325/32
5     48/64
FACE 120/50
OVERHANGING
```

Figure A.7 Computer-generated inclined hemisphere projection for an overhanging face.

N1, N2, N3,...	normals to planes 1, 2, 3,...	Nhr	rotated normal to horizontal (the vertical direction)
D1, D2, D3,...	lines of maximum dip of planes 1, 2, 3,...	HORIZ	the great circle of the rotated horizontal plane
		Dfr	the downward-directed end of the rotated line of maximum dip of the rock face

(b) Inclined hemisphere projection

(N)	north point of original lower-hemisphere projection
N1r, N2r, N3r,...	rotated normals to planes 1, 2, 3,...
D1r, D2r, D3r,...	rotated lines of maximum dip of planes 1, 2, 3,...

The program IHP can plot up to 30 separate discontinuity sets. However, for visual clarity, it is recommended that no more than ten sets are plotted on a single diagram. Figure A.6 is a computer-generated version of the lower-hemisphere projection previously presented in Figure 7.3. Figures A.7 and A.8 are computer-generated versions of the inclined hemisphere projections previously presented in Figures 7.7 and 7.8 respectively. Each projection took approximately 3 minutes to generate and a further 5 minutes to dump onto the printer.

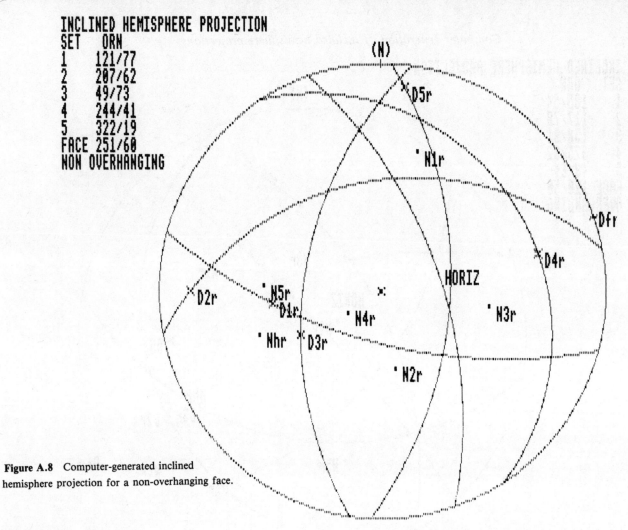

Figure A.8 Computer-generated inclined hemisphere projection for a non-overhanging face.

References

Attewell, P. B. and I. W. Farmer 1976. *Principles of engineering geology.* London: Chapman and Hall.

Brady, B. H. G. and E. T. Brown 1985. *Rock mechanics for underground mining.* London: George Allen & Unwin.

Cartney, S. A. 1977. The ubiquitous joint method. Cavern design at Dinorwic Power Station. *Tunnels & Tunnelling* **9** (May/June), 54–7.

Fisher, R. 1953. Dispersion on a sphere. *Proc. R. Soc. Lond. A* **217**, 295–305.

Goodman, R. E. 1976. *Methods of geological engineering in discontinuous rocks.* St Paul: West.

Goodman, R. E. 1980. *Introduction to rock mechanics.* New York: Wiley.

Goodman, R. E. and Gen-hua Shi 1984. *Block theory and its application to rock engineering.* New Jersey: Prentice Hall (in press).

Hoek, E. and J. W. Bray 1981. *Rock slope engineering,* 3rd edn. London: Institution of Mining and Metallurgy.

Hoek, E. and E. T. Brown 1980. *Underground excavations in rock.* London: Institution of Mining and Metallurgy.

Hudson, J. A. and S. D. Priest 1983. Discontinuity frequency in rock masses. *Int. J. Rock Mech. Min. Sci. & Geomech. Abstr.* **20**, 73–89.

Koch, G. S. and R. F. Link 1971. *Statistical analysis of geological data,* vol. 2. New York: John Wiley.

Krumbein, W. C. and F. A. Graybill 1965. *An introduction to statistical models in geology.* New York: McGraw-Hill.

Phillips, F. C. 1963. *An introduction to crystallography,* 3rd edn. London: Longmans Green.

Phillips, F. C. 1971. *The use of stereographic projection in structural geology,* 3rd edn. London: Edward Arnold.

Priest, S. D. 1980. The use of inclined hemisphere projection methods for the determination of kinematic feasibility, slide direction and volume of rock blocks. *Int. J. Rock Mech. Min. Sci & Geomech. Abstr.* **17**, 1–23.

Priest, S. D. 1983. Computer generation of inclined hemisphere projections. Technical note. *Int. J. Rock Mech. Min. Sci. & Geomech. Abstr.* **20**, 43–7.

Priest. S. D. and J. A. Hudson 1976. Discontinuity spacings in rock. *Int. J. Rock Mech. Min. Sci & Geomech. Abstr.* **13**, 135–48.

Priest, S. D. and J. A. Hudson 1981. Estimation of discontinuity spacing and trace length using scanline surveys. *Int. J. Rock Mech. Min. Sci. & Geomech. Abstr.* **18**, 183–97.

Ragan, D. M. 1973. *Structural geology, an introduction to geometrical techniques,* 2nd edn. Chichester: Wiley.

Spiegel, M. R. 1974. *Vector analysis and an introduction to tensor analysis,* Schaum's outline series. New York: McGraw-Hill.

Terzaghi, R. D. 1965. Sources of error in joint surveys. *Geotechnique* **15**, 287–304.

Thompson, N. A. 1983. *Translational and rotational stability of tetrahedral wedges in rock slopes, using hemispherical projections and vector methods.* M.Sc. dissertation, Imperial College, University of London.

Till, R. 1974. *Statistical methods for the earth scientist.* London: Macmillan.

Warburton, P. M. 1981. Vector stability analysis of an arbitrary polyhedral rock block with any number of free faces. *Int. J. Rock Mech. Min. Sci. & Geomech. Abstr.* **18**, 415–27.

Wittke, W. 1965. Berechnung der Standsicherheit von Felsböschungen. In *XV Salzburger Felsmechanik-Kolloquium, 1964 (Felsmechanik und Ingenieurgeologie* Suppl. II).

Answers to exercises

Chapter 1

1.1 145/18.

1.2 043/63 or 223/63 (trend/plunge).

1.3 026°.

Chapter 2

2.1 (i) 36.9°; (ii) 48.6°.

2.2 (i) 164.7 mm^2; (ii) 48.5 mm^2.

2.3 163/24.

2.4 334/17.

Chapter 3

3.1 257/51.

3.2 (i) 115°; (ii) 068/21; (iii) 150/70 (dip direction/dip amount); (iv) 62°.

3.3 305°, 81°.

3.4 330/82 (dip direction/dip amount).

Chapter 4

4.1 086/29 (dip direction/dip amount).

4.2 (1) 177/21; (2) 336/52; (3) 103/76 (dip directions/dip amounts).

4.3 (1) 056/65; (2) 186/35 (dip directions/dip amounts).

Chapter 5

5.1 Unweighted: (i) dip direction 304.4°, dip amount 51.2°: (ii) 20.35; (iii) (a) 0.266, (b) 0.149.

Weighted and normalised: (i) dip direction 298.7°, dip amount 49.5°; (ii) 19.55; (iii) (a) 0.257, (b) 0.160.

5.2 (i) dip direction 134.5°, dip amount 28.0°; (ii) 41.21; (iii) (a) 4.9°, (b) 6.1°.

Chapter 6

6.1 (i) Trend 158.3°, plunge 33.6°, 15.90 kN, down; (ii) trend 123.7°, plunge 45.5°, 42.36 kN, up.

6.2 − 29.91; 27.89; − 31.95 kN.

6.3 Trend 108.5°, plunge 50.8°, 39.47 kN, down.

6.4 (i) 143.11 kN, down; (ii) 227.72 kN, up; (iii) 50.14 kN, down.

6.5 (i) 117.56 kN, up; (ii) 161.80 kN, up.

6.6 (i) 250 kN, up; (ii) 166 kN, up; (iii) 236 kN, up (approximate values).

6.7 (i) 103 kN; (ii) 29 kN (approximate values).

Chapter 7

7.1

Block	Sliding planes	Sliding direction if unstable (trend/plunge)
1,2,3	falls vertically	–
1,2,4	falls vertically	–
1,2,5	falls vertically	–
1,3,4	3 and 4	177/15
1,3,5	3 and 5	162/45
1,4,5	5	140/48
2,3,4	3	092/72
2,3,5	3	092/72
2,4,5	2 and 5	091/36
3,4,5	5	140/48

7.2

Block	Sliding planes	Sliding direction if unstable (trend/plunge)
1,2,3	2	231/62
1,2,4	1	165/48
1,2,5	1 and 2	177/48
1,3,4	1	165/48
1,3,5	1 and 5	233/23
1,4,5	1	165/48
2,3,4	2	231/62
2,3,5	2	231/62
2,4,5	2 and 4	166/39
3,4,5	5	192/30

If plane 5 were a non-overhanging additional free face, blocks 1,3,5 and 3,4,5 would be invalid.

7.3

Block	Sliding planes	Sliding direction if unstable (trend/plunge)
1,2,3	directed upwards	–
1,2,4	directed upwards	–
1,2,5	5	104/32
1,3,4	4	237/54
1,3,5	5	104/32
1,4,5	5	104/32
2,3,4	4	237/54
2,3,5	directed upwards	–
2,4,5	4 and 5	161/19
3,4,5	4	237/54

7.4

Block	Sliding planes	Sliding direction if unstable (trend/plunge)
1,2,3	1 and 2	309/27
1,2,4	4	303/46
1,2,top	1 and 2	309/27
1,3,4	4	303/46
1,3,top	not valid	–
1,4,top	1 and 4	333/42
2,3,4	2 and 4	264/39
2,3,top	not valid	–
2,4,top	4	303/46
3,4,top	4	303/46

Chapter 8 (All values are approximate)

8.1 (i) (a) $A_f = 24.1$ m^2, $A_1 = 12.5$ m^2, $A_2 = 13.9$ m^2, $A_3 = 15.7$ m^2, $h = 2.92$ m, $V = 23.5$ m^3; (b) $A_f = 59.5$ m^2, $A_1 = 30.8$ m^2, $A_2 = 34.4$ m^2, $A_3 = 38.8$ m^2, $h = 4.59$ m, $V = 91.0$ m^3.

(ii)

	Trend (deg)	Plunge (deg)	Magnitude (kN)	Sense
(a)	–	90	658	up
(b)	305	82	873	up
(c)	–	90	2548	up
(d)	305	85	3077	up

8.2 $V = 17.0$ m^3; (i) trend/plunge 296/40, on planes 1 and 2, $F = 1.8$; (ii) trend/plunge 304/39, on plane 1 only, $F = 0.9$.

8.3 (i) $F = 1.76$; (ii) $F = 1.38$.

8.4 $A_f = 81.5$ m^2, $V = 115.9$ m^3; (i) $F = 1.51$ on planes 1 and 2; (ii) $F = 0.75$ on plane 1 only, sliding direction trend/plunge 010/46.

123

Index

Numbers in *italics* refer to text figures